Alaska Quarterly Review

Vol. 25 No. 1 & 2 ❖   ❖ Spring & Summer 2008

D1065860

UNIVERSITY OF ALASKA
ANCHORAGE

Alaska Quarterly Review is a journal devoted to contemporary literary art. It is published twice each year by the University of Alaska Anchorage, an Affirmative Action/Equal Opportunity Employer and Educational Institution.
Editor Ronald Spatz **Senior Affiliate Editors** Robert Clark, Stephanie Cole **Affiliate Editors** Stacy Smith, Tara Wreyford **Interns** Jonah Hoyle, David Onofrychuk **Contributing Editors** Billy Collins, Olena Kalytiak Davis, Stuart Dischell, Stuart Dybek, Nancy Eimers, Patricia Hampl, Amy Hempel, Jane Hirshfield, Dorianne Laux, Maxine Kumin, Pattiann Rogers, Michael Ryan, Peggy Shumaker **Founding Editors** Ronald Spatz, James Jakob Liszka **Copy Editors** Jean Ayers, Michael Jones **Office Assistants** Jeanette Gabryszak, Nataliya Udovyk

Subscription rates are $18.00 for one year, $36.00 for two years, and $54.00 for three years. Please add $4.00 per year for Canadian subscriptions and $20 per year for subscriptions to all other countries. Sample copies are $6.00 for U.S. and Canada; $16.00 to all other countries. Back issue prices on request. The editors invite submissions of fiction, short plays, poetry, and literary nonfiction in traditional and experimental styles. Unsolicited manuscripts are read between August 15 and May 15 and must be accompanied by a stamped, self-addressed envelope. Send all correspondence to: Editors, *Alaska Quarterly Review,* University of Alaska Anchorage, 3211 Providence Drive, Anchorage, AK 99508.

Web Site *http://www.uaa.alaska.edu/aqr*

Distributors: Ingram Periodicals, 1240 Heil Quaker Blvd., Lavergne, TN 37086
International Periodical Distributors, 27500 Riverview Center Blvd., Suite 400, Bonita Springs, FL 34134
Ubiquity Distributors, 607 Degraw St., Brooklyn, NY 11217
University Microfilms International, 300 North Zeeb Road, Ann Arbor, MI 48106

Alaska Quarterly Review is listed in *The American Humanities Index* and is a member of CLMP.

ISSN 0737-268X

About the cover
Pioneer Peak towers over a farm house and barn near Palmer, Alaska.
© 2008 Clark James Mishler

AQR
Alaska Quarterly Review

Vol. 25 No. 1 & 2   Spring & Summer 2008

CONTENTS

FICTION

NONFICTION

POETRY

Guest Editor: Jane Hirshfield

AQR
Alaska Quarterly Review

Vol. 25 No. 1 & 2   Spring & Summer 2008

Vol. 25 No. 1 & 2   Spring & Summer 2008   Alaska Quarterly Review

Grace Paley
1922–2007

"Everyone, real or invented, deserves the open destiny of life."

This issue of *Alaska Quarterly Review* is dedicated to the memory of Grace Paley, a masterful writer of stories, essays, and poems whose courageous life and works embody the quest for truth and justice in the world.

A long-time contributing editor of *Alaska Quarterly Review*, Grace was a good friend and mentor to us. "Against Despair: An Interview with Grace Paley" and a mini-anthology of her work appeared in Volume 7, Number 3 & 4 (Spring and Summer 1989). Her essay, "Six Days: Some Rememberings," appeared in Volume 13, Number 1 & 2 (Fall and Winter 1994) and was subsequently selected for *The Best American Essays* and *The Pushcart Prize: Best of the Small Presses*. More recently, three of her poems appeared in Volume 22, Number 3 & 4 (Fall and Winter 2005).

FICTION

Kirstin Allio

THE OTHER WOMAN

My mother played piano, Oldies and Chopin. Twice a year she played Happy Birthday – once for me, once for my brother, on the mornings of our birthdays. She would wake up early for it – in order to wake us up, early. The one day she could tease us without risking her life, she said. Hah. You weren't allowed to kill your mother on your birthday. Or get up on the wrong side of bed, geniuses.

Oh it really cracked her up, what her employer had told her. Did you know that Happy Birthday was the first song ever transmitted back to earth from a spacecraft? My brother wanted to know what kind of spaceship and my mother said, No Zack, no. That is not the question. You get a blob of information, Zack, and the question you *don't* ask, is What's this fucking blob of information?

I gave him a glare like naturally I agreed with our mother.

The way you do it, said my mother. You look. For the *why* question.

Professor Shemaria, my mother's employer, saw the world through why-colored glasses. Professor Shemaria connected everything, declared my mother, in her classroom and her research, through why questions. What do you think I do all day, said my mother, empty wastebaskets?

Kirstin Allio is the author of the novel *Garner* (Coffee House Press, 2005).

Is that a why question? said my brother.

Zack's key to life, said my mother. Act so dumb that when you act normal everybody thinks you're a genius.

I hooked my toes on the back of his sneaker so that when he lunged he lost it. Flat tire, genius. We were vaguely – but vigilantly – out to get each other, the three of us.

Nan Shemaria was a professor of sociology. Everything she told my mother about the human race ended up being something bad, something snide, something derisive.

Or something doomsday. Professor Shemaria was politically childless, my mother informed us. You could do an end run around anything, said my mother, with the right term for it.

If why questions weren't already anti-faith, anti-religion, Professor Shemaria's end run around religious holidays was the inauguration of wine and cheese Fridays. On the Department's nickel, reported my mother. Swiss, brie, butterfly crackers, chunks of unripe cantaloupe like something from a dermatology experiment. Adjunct faculty debated Head Start vs. stipends for home-tests administered by stay-home mothers, grad students dangled their theses like undergarments, a pair of precocious undergrads stuck their heads in, only to recoil when they gauged the naked distance across the room to the wine and cheese table.

Fridays my mother got home after midnight.

Our house was a one-story box, like the little green ones in Monopoly, but with a sun porch. My mother rented half the driveway to a neighbor for her son's Yamaha motorcycle. My brother played on the bike incessantly, and my mother yelled through the louvered slats of the sun porch. We were right across the street from Our Lady F, Efraimia, where we did not go to church, because of questions handed down from Professor Shemaria.

"Happy Mor-tal-ity to you, Happy Mor-tal-ity to you! You act like a monkey, 'cause you came from one, too."

Truthfully, was it Happy Birthday? Or death itself that was transmitted from outer space, I wondered. I thought of death beamed down from the same school assembly that divulged the news about the *Challenger*. The air-beyond-the-air that hosted Russian spy pods, and the stars like street lights on a foggy winter evening.

Anyway, my mother played it loud and raucous, on the mornings of our birthdays. She played with exaggerated fermatas, *derisively,* from the sun porch, not an ideal place for an instrument, and she winced and cursed when another mutinous key went flat, or the pedals jammed with humidity.

She sang along, but only in Spanish. Less sentimental to sing in Spanish. Condescending to sing in Spanish. We were basically Italian. Singing in Spanish made our birthdays part of the running joke on the banality of love in families.

My mother was tall and spidery, all transparent joints, high-waisted jeans with long tapered legs inside of which her own legs were pipe cleaners. Her cigarette leaned out of her mouth dangerously – she liked to scare us. She kept a big jar of pennies on the kitchen counter, glass with a thick glass lid, as big as those jars of jelly beans you're supposed to count to win prizes. A gift certificate to Newport Creamery, a shampoo-color-cut-by-Trudy.

Trying to guess the pennies – it made your head spin, like an optical illusion.

My brother and I agreed: for a couple of reasons the pennies were almost impossible to filch. First of all, you didn't have time to count to a hundred. Second, you didn't steal a dollar, you stole a hundred times. A hundred counts of stealing; that was a lot of wrongdoing for a measly dollar! That was the point. That was the hard lesson. Another hard lesson was our father leaving, but our mother was glad, because it proved there was no love in families. Our mother was glad, because it was one more person accounted for by sweeping generalizations. The Alimony Asshole, our father.

Truthfully, he didn't just vanish. That would have been something to talk about, something for which to raise sympathy. But our mother didn't care for sympathy.

He worked at T.F. Green Airport. My brother used to think he *built* T.F. Green Airport. The unions squeezed him – same as my mother, he wasn't a joiner. He was snuck on a construction site in Dorchester. Then there was a gig in Lowell. Each job a little farther from Providence.

We got a long-suffering, bearish stepfather after a while, who our mother teased mercilessly.

Whenever we found a penny – exempting in a public fountain (because Professor Shemaria had catalogued the "wishing well phenomenon"), but on the gummy floor of the supermarket, for instance – we were supposed to pick it up and save it for our mother. All the lost pennies in Providence belonged to our mother. Her eyes were copper. Green spots appeared with her illness.

* * *

My high school yearbook voted me most likely to keep my figure. It wasn't necessarily a compliment. It seemed to me you wanted, at that age, to *spend* your figure.

My mother was balancing on the kitchen counter on one elbow.

The counter was lemon yellow with sparkles – a 1950's dessert, floating island. My mother said the sparkles were mica. Oh it cracked her up, too, how kitchens had evolved from the fucking fire of Prometheus. "You know?" she said. "The Early Peoples actually used three hundred and sixty degrees of their cooking fires." My brother and I rolled our eyes behind her.

The pattern in the tan carpet was like worm tunnels in tree bark.

My mother was idly paging through my yearbook. I remember thinking: What if you were thirty-seven, instead of seventeen, when you graduated? What if you could calmly flip through your yearbook pointing, "Hah. That's-Diane-Orabona's-daughter. I-remember-when-Diane-Orabona-bled/peed/retched-in-gym-class." Or, stabbing at a dumpy girl in a homemade anarchy t-shirt, "Look-at-the-birth-control-boobs-on-that-one!"

My mother talked fast, and she only ever smoked half her cigarette.

She said, "Didn't they lower the hormone dosage? Didn't I read that?"

I laughed nervously.

"In my day birth control was a fucking horse pill."

What if you were a certified know-it-all (my brother added the certification), and you had something to say about everyone? What if, at thirty-seven, you had already had one scare, including chemo, one surgery, and one remission, and you could still say *boobs*? As if you still possessed them?

And how could I laugh with you when you said it?

"They couldn't say anything about your grades?" my mother persisted, thumping the yearbook.

"Hah," said my mother. "Nothing cute about straight A's, is there. Nothing hot about a four-point-o, four years running." That was, indeed, my grade point average.

Why did I choose this moment to notice that my mother had, since yesterday, become flat-chested? My mother, the employee of sociology, had apparently discarded the post-mastectomy bras the insurance company had paid for.

One Saturday morning I found her on the sun porch busy among stacks of papers. The sunlight through the slats blinked maniacally. My mother was kneeling, using the piano bench as a table. Papers were loosely fanned around her. She was furiously marking across the type, and in the margins of what could only be, I thought with horror, school papers. Her left hand was pulling out hairs, strand by strand, a habit of which she was so deeply ashamed my brother and I had never even mentioned it to each other.

"What are you doing?" I surprised her. She snapped back like a measuring tape into its metal locket.

"Maybe you'd like to help me here, genius." She recovered quickly.

"Okay." I didn't move. She beckoned hectically, trying, I could see, to appear impatient.

I tried to look without looking, as if the pages were love letters or a diary.

"She's having me grade papers." My mother's voice went up – she couldn't conceal her excitement. "Intro to Sociology. Her TA had to go home to Argentina."

My mother was grinning. She smacked the page in front of her. "Hah. Anybody could do this."

I reached for one of the stapled packets and I saw that my mother's impulse was to stop me. She caught herself. I looked at it without reading. A college paper. "What?" said my mother. "You don't think I'm up to it?"

I said, "You were supposed to rest – more – I thought."

"Do you see me on my feet?" said my mother. "I'm poolside, genius." She let her big eyes close for a moment. She grabbed a handful of papers and made for the sun porch sofa. She rolled herself out luxuriantly.

"I could do this in my sleep," she said, closing her eyes again, for my benefit.

"I can farm some out to you," she called after me. I couldn't recall ever having heard her so hopeful.

I could live at home and put myself through college. I could choose – two years, secretary, four years, teaching certificate. Never a nurse. I had done my fair share of nursing. Besides, those were girls who smoked since seventh grade, starred in slumber parties, and were now forced to smoke in the wind tunnel against the north side of the hospital annex.

I met Phil because we attended the same teachers' conference in Providence, and he mistook my parked car for his Rent-a-Wreck.

He'd lost the keys and was jimmying ineffectually with a coat hanger. "You know there are demonstrations outside Planned Parenthood against that," I said, sounding for all the world like my mother. He jumped. He made an embarrassing little sound and I blushed for him.

His quavering defense: "Who actually owns a – a – well a Taurus?"

"Girls from Rhode Island," I countered, guessing correctly that he wasn't a native.

Scattered about his feet was a dry fountain's worth of pennies. I pointed. "A hole in your pocket?" I said rash things when I was nervous, I realized, just like my mother.

He ducked; he shook the pockets of his sport jacket; he came up underneath the pockets to gauge the sewing project (not that I knew then he did his own sewing); he stepped out of the constellation of loose change around him.

He gave a surveying look across the sidewalk, and smiled helplessly.

I had to smile back at him. I said, "I guess it won't poison the pigeons."

He laughed, but I could see he was baffled.

"I mean you can't feed the ducks anymore because it's complex carbohydrates," I babbled. "You can't throw an apple core on the highway because a skunk will risk his life for it." He was staring at me, but not unkindly.

"Phil Lebed," he said, holding his hand out. What a round face – and was he cross-eyed behind his glasses?

His hand was as soft as a kaiser roll from the supermarket. What was so odd about him? He talked like a white man, and he was shy like a white man, but his skin was the muted black of an old backyard tire swing.

"What's your name?" he said finally, when I didn't offer it, and – I knew, intuitively – at great cost to his temperament.

Before I could stop myself out came my standard. "Hey, that's what people always ask me." He only looked flustered.

"Swan," I said. "I'm Swan." I was not accustomed to speaking gently.

Between Phil's thick eyebrows and mat of dark hair was a sweatband of tight forehead. His eyebrows kept edging the sweatband upward. "Swan!" he said, clearly delighted.

"Uh-huh," I said, covering my bases.

He put up his arm as if to shield himself. I would have to be even gentler!

A meter maid beneath a baseball cap came sneaking along the sidewalk. I glanced down – yes, she had chalked my tires. I began to fumble instinctively in my pockets even as she stepped back and made to write out a ticket. The nerve. I put myself between her and the meter. Without looking up she said, "Better hurry." I opened my mouth – I was going to lay into her – but out of the blue –

"It's our car," said Phil Lebed, outrageously.

To make a love story short? As of that very moment, I was no longer alone against all the meter maids of this world.

From Rhode Island to the island of Manhattan – Phil was, indeed, a New Yorker – was like jumping octaves. There were actual geological gorges – Phil was a geology teacher. Truthfully. Glacial ravines, used like garbage dumps. The train from Providence bore right through them. Once it stalled (the lights went out, and there was a sighing) and I saw a man sleeping under the pitted girder of the highway above us. He had hung a piece of plastic as a wall between him and nothing. The slope and the tracks made a perfect vortex for eternally blowing garbage. It was hard to shake that off, gliding into Penn Station half an hour later.

But there was Phil, so unguardedly glad to see me. His glasses were yellowed like calluses, his dark hair shiny with lanolin, packed on his round head like a yarmulke. His eyes were not crossed, it turned out, but magnified.

For Phil, I described the view from the train of water: slate and onyx, white birds like paper boats, tawny sea marshes. I told him about the real boats that looked like they'd been shrink-wrapped for the winter, and the beautiful old houses on the water – *waterfront*, the obsession of all Rhode Islanders.

I told my mother, over the telephone, which she was sharing with a dying woman pastor from the Olneyville projects, that Phil did the dishes.

"Do you cook suddenly?" bit my mother.

I hated cooking – just like my mother. Hah. The banality of inheritance in families.

Phil cooked, Phil did the dishes. I wanted to inform her: It's not tit for tat, *Mother*. But I was immediately ashamed of myself. I knew she didn't think that. I knew it wasn't an even exchange, her giving me life and me using it.

She was ignoring me, talking to her roommate. Stupidly, I'd betrayed a trace of self-importance in my marriage, and I was paying for it.

"Hello?" said my mother.

I said, "How's K.C.?" The pastor.

"Here's a coincidence," said my mother. A sudden shift – her voice was rich with feeling. "K.C. majored in geology!"

She didn't say, of course, "Like your husband," but I was fairly certain she was speaking of him – richly. And it suddenly occurred to me that my mother never said anything bad about my husband. My mother! Who founded entire *generalizations* on people she met for five minutes as well as on people she claimed to be friends with, would neither describe nor generalize my husband. She wouldn't reduce him, she wouldn't build him up on the scaffolding of some stereotype. No derisive comment.

I had to try her. "He overcompensates for his masculinity," I heard myself saying.

But had my mother heard me? She cackled, and I could hear K.C. laughing in the background.

I told myself I didn't see how Room 743 could be very funny.

I was leaning on the counter in Phil's and my new co-op apartment. The countertops had no sparkles. They were white and showed every single ring of coffee. Phil had promised to take me to Bear Mountain on the weekend. There was a soil test kit in his backpack. I told my mother I wouldn't be coming to Providence till the following Monday.

I hung up, pretending to be businesslike when a nurse stole her attention with tubes and cuffs, a bowl of ice cubes. I could hear the rustle and slump of a great pile of newspaper the nurse had pushed off my mother's lap unceremoniously. My stepfather always left her the newspaper, which, as she said, deprived her of her only reason for a field trip to the hospital gift shop. At home, my stepfather used to read on his back, feet up, pages splayed across his privates. Sections would slide out for my mother to retrieve, the dog to skid on.

Phil read his newspaper at his desk, back rounded like a drumlin. In a halo of Pleistocene light he was a protective examiner.

* * *

Sumi was "handed down" to us.

As if it were a dowry, a slave auction, I imagined telling my mother, coolly.

"This girl is A++," read the note, with her name, (which I wouldn't forget), and telephone number. It was scribbled on the back of a receipt from Love Drugstore. The previous owner of our co-op had purchased Dramamine, Gatorade, and shoe polish.

"Look at this, Phil," I waved it – it crackled – across the blond and shiny stripes of floor board. The windows were cubes of white electric, and giant squares of light fell on the bare wood beneath them. As newlyweds we only had a few boxes.

I found Phil in the would-be bedroom, looking happily and blurrily about him. His good glasses had been misplaced in the move and these backups were from a high school prescription – thick, milky, safety-goggle plastic. They say when one of your senses is compromised, your other senses kick in to compensate. Not in the case of my husband. He was packed in cotton. He couldn't see, hear, taste (all we'd had for the three days preceding the move was Chinese take-out), or smell (our pores were Chinese. Our clothes and the two towels we'd kept out till the last minute).

I spent part of every week in Providence. I kept the house up for my brother and my stepfather, meaning I made one stop for milk, dog food, toilet paper. Then back on the train, most often with an empty seat beside me on the aisle, as weekday mornings were not a popular time to travel. I was a private capsule, privy to everything. Trackside backyards bearing a family's series of "big purchases," a series of disappointments, aboveground pool, trampoline, boat on blocks, pre-fab tool shed with a single, barren window box. My fleeting association with sandy scrub, folded paper birds on the low water was part of the all around sadness.

One morning while I was on the telephone to my mother – (and the woman pastor, I complained to Phil later) – there was a loud knock on the door of Phil's and my apartment. I hung up, apologetically (although my mother hung up before I could apologize, quick as ever to slip out beneath the weight of emotion), and rushed headlong to answer it.

I peeked through the spy hole to see a woman's face, distorted by the miniature lens, nose first, huge, dilated. I retracted. Could she tell I was looking? Had she heard my eager footsteps, and then the appraising silence as I put my eye to the tiny glass circle?

Somebody must have recognized her and let her into the building. I couldn't tell her from an ax murderer, but I opened the door anyway. I, who could barely cross the street in New York City without blushing, sensed immediately that I must act casual and – somehow – generous with my apartment.

"Sumi Creech?" she said, as if I was to approve a password.

She was white as Elmer's Glue, with tomato-colored blemishes along her cheek bones. She smiled – a space between her small front teeth – but she wouldn't be the type for a conventional handshake. She wore a jersey skirt and an oily-soft, drapey t-shirt beneath which her abdomen showed like a week-old balloon, or the lax pouch of an out-of-work belly dancer.

"To clean your apartment?"

"Oh!" I said, ratcheting up my sisterly smile. "Come in. I was just – "

She moved in on my little apartment.

I shrunk back toward the white counters. There must have been a hundred rings the color of henna, quite beautiful if you didn't think "coffee."

"Did they not tell you I was coming?" said Sumi. She lugged a duffel bag the size of a two week vacation.

"What's in there?" I said, before I could stop myself.

"All homemade solvents." She ticked them off on her fingers. "Vinegar for the glass, grapefruit seed extract for the bathroom, a lot of hemp and aloe vera. I bring my own rags unless you want me to use yours. I don't use paper towel." She squatted down and began to unzip the duffel.

"Wait," I said, and my voice sounded so petulant and superficial that I hated myself as I felt she must hate me – for resisting.

That was it. I did not want her to hate me.

"The thing is," said Sumi matter-of-factly, "I know this apartment. I can do it in under two hours. On this floor I do Harriet's, the Kim's . . ." she trailed off. "If you want to ask anybody."

I studied the view from the kitchen window: all angles and blocks, hues of brick, brick slashed with shadow, baked in sunlight. Sky, brick, street. It was so easy not to see the people.

I tried not to watch her. I tried not to listen to the roar of the vacuum – Phil and I didn't have one, but Sumi had let herself nonchalantly into "Harriet's" (I didn't know any of my neighbors) and borrowed "the beast," as she called it.

When she got around to the kitchen, I retreated to the bedroom. She had picked up all the clothes and folded them neutrally, neatly. She had opened the blinds. How did light find its way down a brick chasm and then L-shaped like a periscope into this window? I stood at the bared glass and looked slantwise toward another brickscape. My apartment was beginning to smell like a humid garden. Was there anything to say to her, if I made it out to the kitchen? Was there anything *not* to say to her?

Now I know you can divide womankind by those who clean feverishly the night before, and those who leave oatmeal parchment curling up the sides of a pot, not unlike dried semen.

Before Sumi's arrival, I arranged flowers in casual mugs and tucked them in private, inconspicuous spots as if I had an easy, spontaneous relationship with my apartment. I secretly hoped she would pilfer some of my expired acne creams – I no longer needed them, being a Mrs.

She cycled around to me on Wednesdays, some time before eleven. I made Phil's and my bed up like a hotel room, even placed an ashtray on the white coverlet. I hadn't smoked since I was fourteen, behind the roller rink, with the girls who became nurses.

I always had the water boiling. While Sumi sipped her tea – cranberry, she had advised me, for urinary tract infections – I discreetly placed the two twenties half in, half out of her patchwork coat pocket.

We talked about Sumi's childhood. Her parents had dropped out in the Seventies. They were back-to-the-landers, a revised farm in the Northeast Kingdom. Vermont, I learned, which was a place I'd never considered. What was it like to pad across the cold crooked floorboards of a vintage farmhouse in the middle of the night to the unlocked door of the outhouse? To meet boyfriends by the pond for skinny-dipping? I imagined them all, the boyfriends, as carpenters, or traders from the nineteenth century.

Sumi's wardrobe – I'd never seen anything like it. She wore anti clothes, I decided, things that were ugly on purpose. But truthfully, was there anything more to style than purpose? Garishly crocheted shawls on top of leotards, peasant blouses stained from breastfeeding, a pair of drafty, unlaced high-tops. Her hair was thin and scabby from veganism, a practice in alignment with her political brand of poverty. She dyed it with a natural plant, and it was an angry, premature gray at the roots. Sometimes she brought her baby, a little twist in tie-dye she called a sling, who swung like a third udder as she cleaned my apartment. "A persistent soul," she said, admiringly. "He's been trying to get in on this world since I was fifteen," she explained to me.

"What's his name?" I asked gingerly.

"Goose," said Sumi. I noticed the baby had red-rimmed eyes like she did.

Of course there was something crackpot about Sumi, but she was so easy to talk to. "I'm like a little ant who was born to hump sand from one hill to another," she said with her gappy smile. How could you be both earnest and cracky? But I was won over.

She took canned goods, loose change, toilet paper, a load or two of laundry detergent in a Ziploc bag like a tiny, blue water bed.

* * *

Phil's mother, Alex, was the famous feminist. I had seen Phil scuttle for cover when our neighbor, Harriet, a lawyer in a margarine colored cardigan over her tennis dress, struck out down the hall ahead of us. Alex had put into Phil a fear of women. Alex didn't believe in marriage: It had the "unmistakable contour of oppression." But what mother believes in the marriage of her only son to the wrong woman? Alex had sculpted, hooded eyes that she blinked slowly (her eyelids had a color all their own – bloodless, lilac), and her burnt-looking hair fizzled at the ends like tassels of an ancient prayer rug. I couldn't decide whether she was ugly or beautiful. I couldn't decide whether I *wanted* her to be ugly or beautiful.

But I thought I knew what *she* wanted – if only I were a bona fide hayseed, pure and oxidized. No. I came from a dissipated line of white zinfandel drinkers, bulk soda in the garage, track suits on the airplane out of Providence.

I was traditional without being original, poor without being humble or spendthrift. I was guilty of putting a post-wedding stretch limousine on plastic. I had whined until my stepfather caved on a penguin of a pianist in a rental tuxedo.

I didn't correct Alex. Truthfully, I hoarded it – the fact that my mother had worked for Professor Nan Shemaria. Had capably – brilliantly? – graded Professor Shemaria's papers. From Professor Shemaria's office windows you could look down over the whole settlement that was Providence. All the barnacled tenements on treeless streets, the state buildings set in over-large parking lots, honeycombed on the inside with countless departments, single windows like fingernails taped to nicotine-stained chambers. Professor Shemaria studied Azorean immigrants. She had my mother staked out at City Hall – my mother was good at striking up conversations with tax drones and coffee-and-donut girls with peroxided Marie Antoinette hairdos. The Azoreans were forced to surface at City Hall eventually, in defense of their lush vineyards which grew miraculously inside a city square of chain link or trained and clipped over a carport.

Professor Shemaria gave my mother a tape recorder with a tiny bud of a microphone. It wasn't necessary to be devious, declared Professor Shemaria, but it was also easy enough to stick the device in a coat pocket. My mother herself might feel more natural if she didn't see it, Professor Shemaria suggested.

I used to imagine that my mother was recording words of wisdom, social prophecy in broken English. Once I found the tape recorder set carefully on top of the piano. My mother was taking a shower, and I swiped it almost without thinking. My thumb squeezed the play button. The tape squealed and clicked off. I fumbled with the little box to turn the tape over.

There was a wall of street noise, loud static of car engines, horns, jackhammering in the background. Where was the dial for volume?

There was a woman's voice, in Portuguese, but I couldn't tell if she was a passerby or a subject. There was another woman cutting in, shrill, "Lena!" I imagined air brakes, a city bus, a near accident. I felt my mother's gaze on me. There she was in the doorway.

"Gendered attitudes toward indigenous agriculture," said my mother dryly. Her long wet hair had soaked her shirt front. I tried to shoot the tape recorder toward her. She took it almost graciously. A half smile: "It's not what they say but why they say it."

Alex was right about the hired pianist.

My mother had always wanted to play at a wedding.

Oldies? Chopin?

She used to joke that she would wear black. What a joke. At Phil's and my wedding she was in a supposed period of remission. But she came in late and sat at the back of the church, a promiscuous ghost among the distant cousins and old neighbors.

At the reception she sweated through her mascara like a maudlin prostitute.

Alex never wore makeup. She smelled like her own sweat. A patchy, backyard smell, raking leaves, flaccid November grass coming off on your sneakers. A foreign smell. I thought about mother animals rejecting their young after the cubs or the kits had been handled by humans.

I couldn't seem to tell my mother about Sumi. I told myself I was thrown by my mother's take on Phil, her uncharacteristic lack of judgment. But I decided to come clean – about Sumi – to Alex. She was grading papers at her kitchen table as Phil prepared a dinner of stir-fried vegetables.

"Safe, Swan?" she said. "Vegetables?"

There'd been a little skirmish the week before. The noodles were made of the same thing as brown paper bags were made of, I'd claimed, pushing my plate toward the center of the table. And I'd gone on, ridiculously, at my mother-in-law's table, that such noodles were "an insult to spaghetti."

To my surprise Alex said lightly, now, and without looking up from her papers, "That's too bad. I wanted to give you Ana Maria."

Twice a week, I learned, Ana Maria let herself in to Alex's apartment in the Village. Her shadow was a wafting blue mist of Windex, her tracks were white as soap flakes. As if by magic, bagels and milk were replenished, the thick dandruff of cat hair dealt to the throaty vacuum, bathrooms transfigured. "She was here today, I think," said Alex.

I excused myself. Indeed, the bathroom shone, all traces of Alex vanquished.

I had to admit I was morally stymied. I had seen the cash Alex left for Ana Maria on the kitchen table – blunt and rumpled.

Maybe, I thought, trying to excuse Alex, being a feminist just meant being busy. But oh, the contradictions. Alex considered her single motherhood a religion, but called herself an atheist. Phil's dad was "a friend of a friend's friend" who agreed on a whim, claimed Alex. And yet hetero sex was never whimsical! It was grave, said Alex. Even violent.

Phil had the same hooded eyes as his mother, luminous gems for pupils, but his skin was dusky instead of halvah. To suppress his rather unmanly giggle, he had the sweetest way of pressing his grape-colored lips together.

He smelled like pie. He was heavy boned and barrel chested. He closed his eyes when he took off his glasses. I rubbed gently around the bone, impossible, in love, to call it an eye socket.

So maybe feminism was just another word for contradiction. I sounded like Alex. Alex would say women were shape-shifters, fluid. If you wore high heeled shoes, you were hobbled by the male race, but there was no race worth running but the male race. High heels or squishy sneakers? Alex would say the question itself was the kernel of feminism. Alex, wryly, "Feminism is all kernel and no flower."

You passed off your broom, your rags, only to enslave another woman. Or were you saving her? From rice and beans in Tijuana? Phil copied his mother, careful to use the name of the city. You never said, Mexico.

Once I heard Ana Maria retching. Alex stood in the doorframe of the bathroom in enormous slappy sheepskin moccasins and a man's dress shirt that came to her kneecaps. Her bare knees were dark and oily-looking with arthritis. Ana Maria's broad back pitched forward so that Alex had to brace herself to hold her. *Now my husband he say no more times. Always you losing the baby.* They lurched like mating insects, hybrid, awkward.

Later Alex told me, "She sat down on the toilet and the baby came out like a pomegranate."

I guess I imagined we were in cahoots, Sumi and I, sharing the load of womanhood. I made the tea while she took a toothbrush to the shower grout. She did my laundry while I made confessions.

For instance, I'd gone off birth control. That was a confession. So many milestones of womanhood have had the taint of shame, secret, I said to Sumi. God, I couldn't bear to remember first menstruating, couldn't even use that word without feeling squeamish. "Sat on a berry?" my mother had said, off-handedly, without looking, or looking elsewhere, so I had followed her gaze across the room instead of to my own body.

Sometimes I lay upon the marriage bed, and listened to the sounds of sweeping and spraying and vacuuming like they were the ocean. By the way, I said once, to Sumi, there was no surf in Rhode Island. It's all bay where I'm from, fish heads and tampon applicators washed up on gravel beaches.

Sometimes I helped her with the other apartments on our floor – inconspicuously – we might have been a coffee klatch or a book club. I pretended I had to keep my hands busy polishing the silver picture frames on Harriet's display shelf. Waterskiing, with a blonde sister (or mother?) in that same tennis dress, a boyfriend with a dinosaur jaw, Washington Square Park – law school graduation. Sumi called her the lawyerette and I laughed conspiratorially, stopping short of telling her how she still terrified Mr. Lebed.

Of course, I had cleaned the house for my mother, I told Sumi. My mother's weakness came in waves. My mother said, with nothing short of disgust, that the nausea was like morning sickness in pregnancy. She said she never wanted to be found dead with her head in the toilet.

When I thought of my mother now, my every motion became obvious, garish. Like finding yourself on very thin ice, in the middle of a lake, in the middle of a nightmare. Even the decibels of your voice crying for help can break it.

My mother's illness? I said to Sumi, my voice hoarse, suddenly, trying out the verdict. A long siphoning of housework, love, money for college.

I had an ancient snapshot that a maternity ward nurse had taken after my birth. "No breast-feeding in Rhode Island!" I declared, as I handed it over to Sumi. Did I want her to feel sorry for me?

I looked at it again, over Sumi's shoulder. There was a crease, white and soft, the stuffing of the photograph, right across my mother's abdomen.

My mother was propped up on the cot, self-possessed enough to have composed a scowl for the camera. The streaked johnny was more or less pasted to the front of her. My father was peeking out from behind her, clutching the paper bag she breathed in to stop hyperventilating. He puked in it later, she once told me.

To Sumi's credit, she studied the picture longer than was required of a mere employee.

"No one's holding you, Swan," Sumi said finally. I grabbed the picture. I suddenly didn't want her to say anything new-agey about hospitals. Sure, I wished my mother could have died in my lap in an authentic farmhouse in the Northeast Kingdom.

But it was true: In the picture, I'm above my mother, as if I haven't even been called down yet. From the heavens – is that how it works, really? Was I a "persistent soul," like Sumi's baby? I'm stranded on my back, on what looks like a metal steam table from a basement cafeteria. I'm one human wail. My red mouth is stretched at the corners, my bluish face contorted.

I imagine my mother rising from the cot coolly. Affixing a pad right to her jeans, no panties, like she always used to. Twisting her raven hair off her neck first, then smoothing it from her forehead.

Raven! Okay, she says to the nurse who snapped the picture. I'll be back later.

* * *

My mother's funeral was the October after Phil and I were married. My brother, living at home, watching football with our stepfather, eating our stepfather's red sauce, which he called gravy, came through, meaning, he arranged it.

Alex offered to go up with us. She said, "Breast cancer is politics."

"Is she going to make a speech? Is she going to run for president of breast cancer?" I asked Phil later.

Phil told Alex we'd go by ourselves. She gave him two pink ribbons to pin on our funeral attire. Breast cancer awareness. I stuck mine in my stepfather's dog's collar.

As if he hoped I would remember our meeting, Phil rented a Ford Taurus.

Alex lounged on Phil's side of the table, books on theory she was sharing with Phil between them. Sometimes she asked me questions thinly disguised as conversation – I knew better than to answer by now if I didn't want to be a case study. I got up and cleared the Saturday lunch away.

In the kitchen I opened my refrigerator in a grand sweep. "Professor Lebed," I called. "Can I get you something?"

"Jam, Swan," came her tuneless voice. She always put it in her tea, like her Russian parentage, slyly asserting herself in my dominion.

But she was striding into the kitchen. I could hear her breasts lapping from side to side, and her hair crackling with static. She kept a bowl of homemade jam in my refrigerator. Now she pulled it out and sniffed the uncovered surface.

"You don't know what to call me, do you," she stated.

"Well, Mother's a little awkward."

"The Other Woman," she said. She moved to toss the spoiled preserves in the garbage. I lunged. Her eyebrows went up.

"I was saving it." Of course, I wasn't.

"I told Sumi to cover it," I said peevishly, before I could stop myself. Alex gave a short, harsh, laugh. I stared hard at the raised mole on her neck that she neglected. Once a month the single hair would have grown long and wiry enough to hopelessly distract me.

I took a long time doing the dishes. "Swan!" called Alex. I came to the doorway. "What was the name of the professor your mother worked for?" I looked at Phil, whose forehead was working. I couldn't be angry with him for defending me. Or explaining me, to his mother. But somehow, I'd wanted her to think I was only track suits and "spaghetti."

"Oh, shoot," I lied, calmly.

"Not by any chance Nan Shemaria – because she did some early work – "

"Truthfully, I never paid much attention."

"Well, no," said Alex, now looking up at me. "You shouldn't have. It was a frustrated life, your mother's."

I couldn't argue with that, although I wanted to beat my mother's life into Alex. "She was always more interested in mine," I retorted.

"That should tell you something."

"Excuse me?"

"That should tell you something," said Alex.

Suddenly, I was livid. "That should tell me!" I was choking. Stiff with rage – I was never agile as a fighter. "I should have been there, Alex!"

"No, you shouldn't have, Swan," said Alex evenly. "You're the daughter, not the attendant."

I turned out of the doorway, disgusted.

But then, all of a sudden, I got it. My mother's strange silence on the topic of Phil and Alex, her suspension of derision. She had hoped these were the people who would take care of me.

In the early evening I was to meet Phil at his mother's department, at a Dean's tea where she was to receive an honor.

Alex was at the center of the coil, her olive green eyes lit by the little amber-shaded university lamps on polished surfaces.

This is years afterward.

I heard Alex bray above the usual mounds of conversation. I thought, Alex has spent her career practicing laughing louder than any man in academia.

There she was, leaning on the cherry podium some "work study personage" – I could just hear her – had dollied in for the occasion. She seemed to sense me watching, and she nodded curtly. She had been hoping, I supposed, that Phil and I had come together.

An x of a woman – cinched waist, flared, Victorian collar – was heading toward me. I hadn't counted on talking to anyone. The woman's features were deep notches – I imagined when she fit her face to another face it would sort of lock in for the duration. Like mating for life, now that was a picture. As she came closer I decided she looked like Abigail Adams, first lady, with a beak chin and a kind of sly, fetal old Englishness.

"You must be the Double Swan," she said, holding her hand out.

The Double Swan! What Phil called me. Lebed meant swan in Russian. She had an overly firm grip. She shook my hand as if women had been doing it for ages.

"Nan Shemaria."

Of course, I started. Nan looked for Alex. She waved and gestured – pointing to the crown of my head – when she caught Alex's attention. Alex was already striding toward us.

"So?" said Alex.

Nan's nose and chin squeezed together like pincers. "You look exactly like your mother," she informed me.

Alex stepped back and squinted.

I stood very still, under their consideration.

"Shall we sit?" Alex directed us. I followed with my teacup to a university upholstered sofa. A grad student of Alex's – effete, fleet, and fawning – passed by with a tray of wineglasses filled one-third with red brown liquid. I traded in the teacup.

"Here's to you, Alex." Nan raised her glass in the same way she had shaken my hand – as if toasting had always been women's provenance. People were watching. These two small women were heavyweights in their fields. My skin prickled. There was the Dean, blundering toward us expectantly, burnished with alcohol. Alex rose to greet him. I cast my eyes around for Phil. What was keeping him?

Nan exhaled loudly. "Such an intimate setting." She waved at the faux living room. Now, pointing to my wineglass, "You might want another one before you hear this." God, I thought. The two of them had the bedside manner of 1950's male gynecologists.

Then Nan said, "Did your mother ever mention our relationship?" She couldn't help herself. I raised my eyebrows.

"Casablanca," said Alex.

Truthfully, she *uttered* it. And I wanted to laugh, perversely. What a ridiculous name. People called her Cas – her driver's license said Catherine.

"It amazes us, Swan," started Alex. "That a cleaning lady – a janitor – a single mother, would volunteer in Nan's early research."

"No, I'm sorry, she begged," Nan interrupted. "I was always working late, you know, tripping over her vacuum, and one night she just pleaded."

"Come on, Swan. She must have told you something," said Alex.

"Passing herself off to her own family as my – what did she call herself? I'd be so curious . . . My secretarial assistant? The same house – she must have stowed her uniform in the lockers. Or paid another girl to take it home and wash it?"

"The contraband uniform," said Alex.

Nan snapped her fingers, remembering something. "The uniforms all had name tags!" Nan patted her breast to show the location.

"Nan calls her Lucy," said Alex, with a little stain of a smile. "I just call her the Ur-feminist."

I waited. How they longed for my shock, and my remorse at not having known my own mother.

"We didn't call her Casablanca," I said, finally. "And I used to wash and iron the uniform."

The two women professors were silent.

Truthfully, Nan gawked and Alex swallowed. I had to swallow too, my laughter.

I had to swallow my mother's laughter.

* * *

"Either of you geniuses been digging around in my pennies?"

My mother is cawing. She's holding the big glass jar up like she's about to smash the clay tablet. Not just her voice, her whole face is hoarse, full of catches.

I'm stricken for a long, awful moment. Did I do it or did I only dream I did it?

"This other woman at work?" says my mother. The jar is too heavy to hold up over her head much longer. Like an old freight elevator it jerks and drops down to the counter. "Fresh from the fucking Azores. Skinnier than I am." She pinches her waist, which is like a windpipe. "She doesn't have papers – she's covering for her aunt. That's the word. They all cover for each other. We're in the big closet in Tabor Hall together. I have to show her how to change the mop head. Tina, I say. We call them all Tina, I don't know how it started. She's dragging the Medusa out of the gray water. Her people are fishermen. It's like she's hauling a whale. She says to me, 'Back in the Azores, I have small sons and daughters.' How old is she – thirty? 'I'm savin to bring em hea-ah. I'm workin and savin.'"

My mother pats the counter till she bumps into her cigarettes. "I can't do that weird accent."

"But you know, geniuses?" says my mother, her voice rising. "Wait till she sees this piggy bank." My mother nods at the glass jar. "Not that she's going to be able to lift it."

Matt Bondurant

BIRTHMARK

My mother was yelling because she didn't want us to go to the convict rodeo.

Nettie, my dad said, it ain't gonna do a damn thing to her.

The convict rodeo is all guys who are locked up and my dad says they make the best cowboys and there isn't anything wrong with watching a good rodeo. I don't blame him for thinking so. My dad didn't know that we'd see a convict get stabbed through the heart as he lay in the mud.

Quit cussin' in front of my little girl, my mother says, and slams the screen door.

My dad is drinking beer at Ginny's and I'm looking at pictures of dead people taped to the wall. We left in the morning in my father's work truck. We had the whole day, he said, which was surprising as my dad normally worked Saturdays. He runs his own refrigeration business, fixing people's air conditioning, freezers, things like that. In Texas this is big business, because everybody has a refrigerator and everyone has air conditioning, except maybe the Mexican kids on the

Matt Bondurant's fiction has appeared in *Glimmer Train, Prairie Schooner,* and *The New England Review.* His first novel, *The Third Translation* was published by Hyperion, 2005.

east side. My dad's truck has a ladder rack and long metal lockers in the back that lock with these heavy padlocks. The tools he has inside are expensive, and people will try to steal them. Before we leave the house he heaves a bag of ice on top of a twelve of Coors in the big cooler that's bolted in the bed. The truck seat is ripped and there are bits of paper on the floor, chew spit, and flattened beer cans. He cut the seat belts out with a razor. The truck smells like his shop: burnt grease and the smell men give off when they ride around in trucks all day and fix things. It is the smell I have known all my life.

Quick pit stop, my dad says as we pull into the parking lot at Ginny's Little Longhorn Saloon. Ginny's is just a few blocks from our house. I say, sheesh, because it is ten in the morning and we haven't even gone anywhere yet. Ginny's is just a rinky-dink cinder block joint with doors in the front and back and usually they have them both open and when you walk in you can see right out into the back parking lot and the dumpsters. There is an orange longhorn head painted on the front, kinda like the University of Texas longhorn but a little off, like it wasn't done quite right. The doors are huge and heavy and made of metal, like a mini-fortress. The crazy thing about Ginny's is that no matter what time we go, there are always these people sittin' in there, a row of them at the stools, at the sticky little tables, and the jukebox is always playing the kind of whiney country song my father likes.

While my father orders beer I look at the "Gone But Not Forgotten" wall. It's this section of the wall beside the bar where they have all these Polaroid pictures taped to the wall with things written along the bottom. Things like: "Terry Hoggle 1901–1972. We will miss the jokes and laughter. Miss you Terry." And it's this picture of some old guy in a dirty ball-cap with a cigarette coming out of the side of his mouth and his face all screwed up at the camera like he's thinking *what the hell is this contraption they've got pointed at me now?* They've got twenty-six of these pictures on the wall and I always check to see if there is someone new. The last one to go was a guy named Bud who looks so old in his picture that he ought to be in a hospital somewhere rather than hanging onto the bar with a pitcher of beer in front of him. "Bud 1891–1969." That's all Bud gets so I figure he must have been quite a dud as a live human being.

There is no one new today so I do my next thing which is to inspect the various people at the bar and try to determine who will be next. This is difficult because there are a lot of good candidates. Everybody smokes here, and most of the people are old, much older than my father, or at least just old-looking, some with canes or discolored patches on their faces or flabby bags of skin that hang under their necks like water balloons. They have the kind of faces you would never recognize if you saw them in the street or without a beer in their hand. There is a gray, foggy quality to their bodies and hair, like stuff left in the bottom of the closet, like they are already getting ready to disappear.

My dad has a pitcher of cold Lonestar in front of him and he's drinking with a real content look on his face. Ginny has bowls of ice and glasses set out on the counter with sodas for set-ups and people dip their crusty hands in and grab handfuls of cubes to chill their drinks. A man with long jowls the color of paste and a freckled scalp rubs the back of my neck and says: *hey there Katy!* People know me here, and I'm thinking that we need to stay away from Ginny's as we get older, because apparently a lot of people come here to die. How does Ginny know anyway? She's just a fat woman with a pile of curly hair and glasses with rhinestones on them. What happens when she breaks out the camera and tries to take your picture? Can you run for it, maybe still escape?

One time a few years ago Ginny took a rag and tried to rub my face. I was quick and she didn't get it on me. I have a reddish birthmark on my cheek that people always think is food or something. If you look up close the birthmark is shaped like a tiny hand. When I get mad or sweaty it'll flare up red, and in the winter it will look almost blue. My older sister Dianne, who is away at college in Virginia, used to tell me that it was the mark of an angel who touched me when I was born. I know better now but I let her believe it. My sister is eleven years older than me, with no one in between. She only comes home on holidays, when she has to, and mostly she hunkers around the kitchen in her sweatshirts and old jeans, sighing and arguing with my mother. Sometimes I think that my parents must have been crazy to have another kid, so far apart. But mom says they just wanted to wait for me, for the right kid to come along. As if having children is like waiting for a bus.

My dad uses the tongs to pull a hunk of pickled pig knuckles out of the jar on the counter. The jar is always full of knuckles and eggs, and sometimes I'll stare into the jar real close and try to count the eggs, which is nearly impossible. Sometimes I'll think of the pigs and what they would think if they knew their hands and feet were gonna end up in this jar on the bar of Ginny's Little Longhorn Saloon in Austin, Texas. That's no kind of pig heaven.

My dad almost never talks to anyone at Ginny's; he drinks a few beers and then puts a bunch of dimes into the jukebox. I like George Jones okay, but on TV he is real odd looking with those fat sunglasses and he always seems to be singing with and about women who are clearly so much better looking than him. A sad man. My dad doesn't get sad though; he smiles this strange little smile as he drinks his beer and stares over the bar and ruffles my hair with his hand and we listen to George complain about something. Women wearing more makeup than you will ever see outside of the circus drink glasses of warm vodka without removing the cigarette from their mouths. The sign over the bar says: "Happy Hour 9–5PM." I may be only twelve, but I know that these people don't go to regular work. Two guys shoot a game of pool that will clearly never end. Then my dad's pitcher is empty and the jukebox has shifted to some other poor whining fool and we are finally out the door into the hot sunshine.

We get to the rodeo arena just after noon and I'm fired up to see some bulls. But the bulls don't come on till later so we drop the tailgate in the parking lot and sit a bit, my dad having a chew, and me holding the Beechnut bag for him. It's something we've done for as long as I can remember, sitting on the tailgate, holding my dad's chew while he munches on it thoughtfully and squints into the sun. My dad has loads of lines around his eyes and mouth, and he's always a deep cinnamon color. My mother tries to get me to cover up my skin but I can't be bothered and most of the time I'm the color of a peanut, though nothing like my dad. He's on a lot of big roofs, standing on black tar, all day long.

The parking lot is mostly full, and people are walking past us to the rodeo. Loads of cowboy hats, which you don't see in Austin too much. I don't mention how we missed half of the rodeo already. The early events are a bunch of mush, barrel racing and stuff like that. Who wants to see some girl in a red fringed blouse with stars all over it going around barrels on a horse? Why don't they just get rid of the girl, and have the horses all race at once, that would be something I'd like to see. When I was a little kid my father used to try and get me to do the lil' wrangler bit with the sheep. Like I want to climb on some greasy sheep and get dragged through the mud? I can turn more cartwheels than anyone in the seventh grade and I'm always picked first for kickball. I could've won any sheep-riding contest easy. I've got my University of Texas hat on, pulled down tight and my hair in two small braids. The sun is punishing, but I don't mind it. A lot of people wear sunglasses around. Me and my dad don't. Sunglasses are for babies and people from Dallas.

As we are walking toward the arena doors my dad points out the prison buses, which look like regular school buses painted black and white and with chicken wire around the windows. A fat guard sits on the doorway steps with a shotgun across his knees, eating a baloney sandwich. He gives me a short nod, his cheek bulging like a baseball.

There is a roar from the crowd in the arena and we know someone has either fallen or been hit or failed in some way, because that is what people cheer for at rodeos like this.

Luckily the arena isn't full, and we only go about halfway up the metal bleachers to find a spot. My dad takes the three beers he has in his pockets and sets them between his feet. On the arena floor several rodeo clowns are chasing a bucking horse. There are men in uniforms and mirrored sunglasses standing around the tops of the arena carrying rifles with scopes. The Mexican guys are walking around on the dirt path in front of the stands, their brightly colored shirts pressed flat and their new jeans have sharp creases. The Mexican guys always have the biggest belt buckles, but that's because they are the original cowboys, something Mr. Bingman told us in school when we watched a filmstrip about Mexico. Mr. Bingman has been all over the world and he knows more things than I knew existed. He's just a little string-bean guy with short ties and a knobby chin, but he's the only teacher I really listen to.

I just finished my first year at junior high and I can tell you the whole thing stinks. Except for Mr. Bingman's science class, I wouldn't have anything to do with it. My big sister Dianne says that junior high is just something you have to get through, and then it gets better in high school. In high school you can start to develop the woman you want to be, Dianne says. I doubt it. Last Christmas Dianne also said that our parents didn't love each other any more. I said: Big deal.

Saddle-bronc riding is the next best thing to bulls. Sometimes a horse will turn on a man and kick him good, a double-shot of horseshoes and hooves, but its nothing like when a bull gets around, facing a man on the ground, and you know he's going to go at him with those long curved horns and your stomach seizes up. I'm always rooting for the bull and I don't think there is anything wrong with that. You think these animals want to be out there getting ridden and roped and tied up like that? You would have to be a dope to think otherwise. Like when my dad watches football on television and I ask him who he is rooting for, he always says the underdog. Like to see the little guy win, he says. My dad's eyes follow the clowns as they scramble in the mud, little darting movements and I've always thought that my father has the most beautiful gray eyes and I'm lucky to have them too, instead of dirt brown eyes like my mother and the Mexicans and most people in Texas it seems. He drinks his beers, his lips puckered on the can for a moment, then his big Adam's apple working as he swallows. I have to think he is happy. I grab his hand and he says, hey there squirt.

There's some steer wrestling going on which I don't watch much because I don't like the way they twist the necks of the steers, wrenching their nose around and how it makes their body flip hard to the ground. Instead I watch the stalls where the convict cowboys mill around, waiting for their turn. There are guards in there with them, but they don't seem to be watching them too closely. The convict cowboys all wear the same outfit, grayish pants and shirts and black cowboy hats. The guys who are waiting to ride are wearing leather chaps, but most of them are just hanging out, sitting on a row of benches, smoking cigarettes, hanging onto the metal fence and watching the action in the arena, a couple of them scanning the crowd like they are looking for someone. When they take their hats off to wipe their faces I can see the white skin of their shaved heads, the snaky ink of tattoos on their forearms. I wonder if their families or friends are here, if that was something you did when your brother or father was in prison; you went to see him saddle-bronc at the rodeo.

In Mr. Bingman's science class we watch film strips of butterflies coming out of cocoons and chimpanzees grooming each other. Mr. Bingman's got a mustache like a hairbrush and his hair is all shaggy on top like he forgets to comb it and he says things to us like: you are all glorious golden angels born and transformed from rutting animals and don't you forget it! And I don't.

I brought in a praying mantis I caught in the back yard and we spent a whole class watching it munch the head off a cricket. Then my mantis cleaned its mouth with its elbows, like it was some kind of neat freak contortionist. Mr. Bingman says that in nature things are settled with bloody tooth and claw. Victory is merely survival. Janey Bishop shook her head and made goofy eyes when he said it but she's a dang cracker idiot who wears buckled shoes and can't even really read. I know what he means. The world is like a cloudy day at church with a loop of wire around your neck and somebody other than you think has a hold of the other end.

After the steer wrestling, the convicts get on the bulls and that is where the action begins. We cheer for the first bull rider who gets a full ride and leaps off the back of the horse into the mud, going into a backward roll and then on his feet. The sleeves of his convict shirt are cut off ragged and even from up here you can see the ropey muscles. When I clap my hand on my dad's knee I can see the glassy look in his eye and I know he's had the right amount of drink. I've been watching my father drink for years and clearly there is a "right" amount and then a "wrong" amount and I can tell he is almost always shooting for that right amount. I can even tell when he is upset that he missed it, and gone and had too much or too little and whatever that is happening up in his head isn't right and he growls and shakes his head like a sleepy dog or just gets quiet and uptight about things. He works twelve hour days most of the time and some nights he is so sore he can't do anything but sit in a chair, a glass of Jack Daniels in one hand, and stare at a tiny space in front of his eyes. But when his face relaxes and his eyes get watery he's on the right track. He looks happy, and he smiles and laughs quietly at nearly anything I want him too. My mother gets on him about it but it is at these moments when I love him most and I can tell he loves me.

The convicts don't seem to be afraid at all, they jump right on the bull in the pen even as it's thrashing around and off they go, spinning in the mud. Sometimes it seems that some of these guys have never done it before; they don't even know where to put their hand, and I can see the other cowboys showing them. I ask my dad about it and he says that yeah, some of these fellas probably never been on a bull before, but they do it because the prison gives them special privileges if they do.

Like what kind of privileges? I say.

Could be anything, dad says. Extra recreation time, access to visitors, extra cigarettes, whatever.

I'm thinking I just can't believe that any of those things would be worth getting on a monster bull with wicked horns like they got here. Maybe there is something he isn't telling me. Like maybe if they ride the bull to the buzzer they get out of jail.

The fourth guy out gets launched and then the bull stomps on his chest with his back legs a few times before the clowns can get to him. My dad puts his arm around me but I give him a smile to show that I don't give a fig and it don't bother me at all. They carried that fella out on a stretcher and the next convict jumped up quick onto a mottled black and white bull named Just A Dream and you know its going to be bad and the crowd feels it and people are up and shouting. The gate opens with a clang and the announcer says *here we go!* and that bull comes out sideways about five feet off the ground. Just A Dream ducks its big horny head and the convict goes over the front quick, like he was dumped out of the sky. He crumples on the ground and the bull is on him, hooking at him with his long curved horns and the clowns are waving blankets in his face but Just A Dream pushes him along the ground for a bit, the convict hanging onto his head with both hands, before the bull loses interest and trots back to the open gate. The people around us, skinny guys in tight jeans and blinding white t-shirts, beers in hand, they turn and laugh and slap hands with each other as the convict gets to his knees, holding his side, then limps off to the convict pen. The couple in front of us, an old-timer

and his white-haired wife all gussied up in country line-dancing outfits with gold tassels, don't seem too happy. The old man takes off his
hat and scratches his bald head and the woman shakes her elaborate
hairdo, her mouth drawn up with lipstick in an odd smile. I say I want
to get a hot dog 'cause I'm starved and he gives me a few dollars and
I figure I can watch the bulls from somewhere else and no one has to
think a little girl is getting twisted from watching convicts get
stomped.

The concourse area is just a cement path halfway around the
arena with a few vendors selling fake cowboy gear, the walkway covered in popcorn and beer cans that crunch when I walk over them.
The snack bar is mostly empty seeing as everyone wants to see the
bulls. The crowd roars and I get a dog and a Coke from a lady behind
the counter who is so dried up and dark she looks like something
you'd see in a filmstrip about the Amazon. When I turn around
there's these two runty boys about my age in ridiculous cowboy hats
and brand new Wrangler jeans and they are looking at me kind of
sideways and nudging each other. I'm holding my dog and I sip the
Coke and just watch them squirm for a bit. I see them glancing at my
face and I'm thinking they are going to say something about my
birthmark. I can feel it blazing, like someone holding a miniature
little hot hand on my cheek, but there's nothing I can do about it. The
arena is warm and maybe it's the bull-riding but I feel ready and I
think about how I will throw my Coke in their faces if they say anything about it.

So, the one kid says, searching for words. You a Longhorn, huh?

It's my hat, and I know right off that these idiots are Aggies.

Yeah, I say. So?

Well, the kid says, looking around. Aggies gonna kick your tail
again this year.

I refuse to be drawn in to this. If you live in Texas then this happens all the time.

How? I say, and this confuses them.

Finally the other one bursts out: Football!

Big deal, I say.

I do love Longhorn football, but A&M has been whipping us lately
and I'm not going to even let on that I know that.

Big deal?

They are incredulous. Aggies are always like that. They think
everything lives and dies with football. They wear their Wranglers
and hats and kick around their dusty town in snakeskin boots like it's
the center of the world.

You guys dress like that at school? I say.

Sometimes, they say together.

I got better things to do, I say, and leave them flat.

There are a few bulls left and one convict actually gives it a decent ride, arm flapping, his hat flying off and the buzzer goes and everyone cheers. My father is sipping his last beer, the other two empty cans crushed beneath his boots. Down in the arena they are rolling out a circular card table and some chairs. I'm wondering if my sister Dianne gets to see a convict rodeo in Virginia, and somehow I doubt it. She says her college is the oldest in America and has tons of old buildings covered in ivy full of really smart people. People like us, she tells me one night. Dianne says she finally feels a part of things there, that people understand her. It is one of the best colleges in the world, though I know it isn't better than UT. That's where I'm going.

Last Christmas break Dianne came home and for days we went shopping together or went to the Flight Path Coffee Shop to read books. She made a big deal about mom sleeping on the couch, where she's been sleeping for as long as I can remember.

It's sad, Dianne said to me. That's not the way married people are supposed to live.

How do you know? I said.

Listen, Katy, she said, you want to remember this so you never do this to your family. You can't allow it to happen.

How? I said.

Mom and dad got married at nineteen, Dianne said. They didn't know better. It was good at first, as it usually is. They were happy once, but they aren't any more. It was a mistake.

There's us, I said. Isn't that something?

My sister is tall and beautiful and she's the smartest person I know other than Mr. Bingman. But she doesn't know everything.

Ladies and gentlemen, the announcer rumbles, *it is now time for that most dangerous card game . . . place your bets . . . it's convict poker!*

People in the stands whoop and cheer and I ask my dad what this is about but he doesn't answer, he just stares out over the crowd, his face like stone. His eyes have lost their wet look and I'm thinking he may have lost the right amount. The clowns set up the table and six chairs and six convicts come trooping out in their matching outfits. Right away I can tell some of these guys are out there because they have no business on a bull. One fellow was at least three hundred pounds, and there are two skinny black guys. Another man was wearing glasses, a funny thing to do in the rodeo, and he was walking real unsteady, his pantlegs flapping. These six guys take a seat and pick up the cards and deal and then start playing poker like you've never seen. I mean they are picking up and throwing cards, like some kind of speed poker.

Ladies and gentlemen, here we go! Introducing our final player: Here comes King Deuce!

The gate swings open and a pale gray bull comes trotting out. King Deuce has a hump on his back like a beach ball and he swings a look over at the convicts playing cards and then trots around the side a bit, checking out the edges of the arena. This bull's horns must be three feet long at least, and they have a load of curve to them. The men at the table don't even look, just keep dealing and throwing them down and I know they aren't really paying attention to the cards. The bull seems to notice them again and turning his big head begins to trot over to the card players and the crowd stands up. He comes up behind them and still the men don't turn around until the bull is right there and then one of the black guys pops up like a jackrabbit off his chair and makes a dash, the bull right on his heels, the clowns bouncing around flapping blankets and things.

I inspect the convict with the glasses, sitting ramrod straight, his elbows close together on the table, chin tucked to his chest, holding his cards with both hands. I can tell he is clenching his jaw to keep his mouth from hanging open. He has thin white arms and pointy fingers and doesn't seem like much of a convict. He looks like one of those people in Ginny's, who could be any age at all but you wouldn't know because they are preserved with booze and cigarettes like an insect in amber. Mr. Bingman brought in a mosquito in a smooth marble of amber to class one time, and he told us that it was over five thousand years old. Mr. Bingman said he carried the thing around in his pocket, like a good luck charm. Janey made her goofy eyes and whispered that everyone knows the *earth* ain't even that old, much less some mosquito. Sometimes I'm not sure Janey knows the difference between something alive and something dead. Brush your teeth sometime, I told her. Mr. Bingman let me rub the golden ball between my fingers and inspect it real close, and I couldn't help but think about the world that this mosquito knew back then, how much different it must have been. I asked how it got in there and he told me that it was just sitting on a tree in South America one day and a drop of tree sap fell on it and that was it. Now nobody hates skeeters more than me, and I'd kill them all if I could. But I liked to think this one didn't really know what was happening to him, he didn't know that he'd end up getting handled by a bunch of kids at McCallum Intermediate or spending most of his time inside Mr. Bingman's linty pockets, or in a change dish on his dresser at night. Frozen for five thousand years, in that same sprawled pose, and for five thousand more.

When King Deuce comes back again he just rams his forehead straight into a guy's back, jamming him against the table, the long horns curved around his shoulders, spilling cards everywhere. This guy hits the ground on all fours and goes under the table and out the other side, the bull circling around the table following him. The convict with glasses does a funny little shrug when the bull passes him but then he seems to calm down and picks up some fresh cards, his mouth set in a line. He has a long, squarish skull and nose that bends in the middle. His long fingers flutter as he holds his cards. I figure I need to rethink the underdog situation. This convict doesn't look like he could do much damage even if he had a shotgun in one hand and a stick of dynamite in the other.

King Deuce comes up slowly and just starts nosing at a guy's elbow who's trying to deal. You can almost see the bull making up his mind, and when he snorts and rears up a bit, the dealer and another guy bolt, tossing their cards in the dirt. The crowd boos as the clowns jump in front of the bull and in the bleachers in front of us the men in the blinding white shirts laugh and punch each other in the back. Now it's just the skinny poke with glasses, the fat guy who is busting out of his convict uniform, and the second black man left, who is bobbing his head in a funny way, like he's saying yes yes yes yes as the fat man deals another hand. They get all their cards before the bull charges again and with a thrust of his horns the bull flips the table high into the air, end over end like a coin. The chubby convict goes sprawling, his chair busted, speed-crawling for the fence, the last two men still sitting in their chairs, holding their cards like nothing happened, the black man's head bobbing faster like a deranged bird. The table lands more than ten feet away and the bull spends a moment or two stomping on it for good measure as the clowns scamper about in their patched overalls and straw hats.

Now you can see the legs of the remaining convicts, and the black man looks like he's dancing sitting down, his legs just flailing out there. The convict with glasses is just vibrating in waves, like he's sitting in a cold draft, his loose pantlegs rippling. They just don't seem like the right fellows to be doing this. The other convicts in the holding pen, hanging onto the rails and watching, smoking cigarettes and their sleeves cut off, tattoos blazing, most of them are clearly bigger and stronger and tougher than these two stickpins. But there they are, holding their cards with dancing feet. For extra cigarettes and a few more minutes in some dismal concrete prison yard?

I poke my dad's leg. What's the deal, I say.

And he looks over at me and gasps like he's surprised to see me sitting there next to him. His lips move funny and he reaches his arm around and takes me close to him and I push my face into his chest and watch with only one eye as the bull lurches at the convict in the glasses and dipping his head hooks him hard with a sideways wrench, tossing him off his chair like a doll. The convict lies crumpled there on his stomach, his glasses gone, and he reaches one hand out and pats the ground slowly, like he's feeling the earth for moisture, his fingers tracing lightly, his legs sprawled out, one pantleg tugged up revealing a bone-white calf that doesn't look any bigger than my arm. Then the bull is on him and I can see the horn sink neatly into his back like a stick pushed into mud.

The crowd goes mostly quiet save some whispered cursing. *Damn, you see that? God damn he got stuck! Damn old boy got it good!* I'm holding my dad tight and thinking of those stupid Aggies at the concession stand, Mr. Bingman and his slides of long, dark rivers in Africa, lime green frogs with red eyes, dusty monkeys playing in the leaves, a mosquito locked in the golden embrace of forever. My father holds me tight and he's whispering in my ear but I can't hear him because I'm crying because it's not like I saw the horn go into that man's back, it's more like it was always there and we didn't know it.

The old woman in the line-dancing outfit is wiping my face with a napkin and I let her because my nose is running fierce. The golden fringe under her arm brushes against my cheek. Everyone seems a bit dazed and the sound in the arena seems muted and lost, like everyone just woke up at once. After a while they are dragging out a stage with a drum kit into the center of the mud and these four guys get up with guitars and cowboy hats. I never even saw them carry him out.

The announcer comes over the PA and there is a weak cheer and when the lights come down the band begins to play. The small circular stage rotates slowly and a series of colored lights play over them and then go shooting off across the crowd. People start to warm up to it, coming back to life, and the men in white t-shirts, glowing in the purple light, wrap their arms around each other like they are brothers and sway together, belting out the lyrics. A spinning mirror ball from the ceiling is lit up with spotlights and little flecks of light go flying around over us, so much like snowfall that I can't help but hold out my hands to catch it. The Mexicans stand straight in their pressed jeans, immaculate pearl-snap shirts, holding hands with their dark-haired girls and the old folks in front look into the lights like they are little children remembering something. I have my hand around my dad's neck and he is smoothing my hair as I watch the band playing their sad songs. Everyone seems to have forgotten the convict with the glasses. The music makes me think of the people in Ginny's Little Longhorn Saloon, how close to death they are at every moment. I'm standing there listening to my father's music and the voice of the sad and lonely cowboy sounds like something new to me, something strange and beautiful.

That night in bed I hear my mother's shuffling footsteps in the living room. She made chicken and biscuits for dinner and my father went right to bed, woozy and red-faced from food and beer. He will get up early tomorrow and go to work, as he never takes off both Saturday and Sunday. I can hear the gentle swish of sheets and blankets as my mother arranges her bed on the couch. I think of my mother in the morning, neatly folding her blankets and pillow up on the couch, putting them into the closet, making coffee as my dad rattles out the door to work.

I will tell my sister Dianne about this next time she is home. When she is home Dianne sleeps with me in my bed and we whisper in the darkness and in the morning her skin is hot and the covers thrown off onto the floor. I will tell her about the skinny convict with the hole in his heart and how he held himself so straight at the table. Thinking of this makes me realize that I miss my sister so badly, more than anything. In the dark I will whisper to Dianne that our father is still in love with our mother and she will murmur, *yes, yes, I see it now,* her eyelids smooth as we fall asleep.

Celeste Ng

B & B

In the summer she misses the chalk. Pink chalk is a treat, dissolving on her tongue with a sweet effervescent hiss she can feel on the back of her throat. She imagines it resembles champagne, almost fruity, floating against her palate. But it is hard to come by. White chalk is more widely used, more plentiful, like bread. She never takes the whole stick, only the ground-down nubs too short to use, so each time the teacher dusts his palms on the back of his jacket she mentally measures the remaining piece. It is hard to wait. She has developed a technique: as the other students file out at the sound of the bell, she trails along after, dragging her hand along the tray at the base of the blackboard, sliding the stub of chalk along the groove until it hits the end and pops into her hand. In the hallway she slides it into her pocket, to be savored on the long walk home, and licks the dust from her fingers.

But in the summer there is no chalk. One year, on the last day before vacation, she stole a full box of chalk from a teacher's desk drawer. She had planned to ration it out, a quarter-inch per day, to last until the fall. But the weight of it in her pocket was irresistible. On the way home from school she stopped off in the park and crunched stick

Celeste Ng's fiction has appeared in *One Story*, *Crazyhorse*, and *TriQuarterly*.

after stick until the whole box was gone. She could buy chalk; she's fifteen, she gets ten dollars a week allowance. But chalk handed across the drugstore counter just isn't the same. So in summer she makes do with other things, anything with that starchy taste: cash register receipts, plaster, subscription cards filched from her mother's decorating magazines. The best are the Better Homes and Gardens; she likes to nibble at the tiny photographs of beautifully dressed and empty living rooms. She's done this since she was a child, and she knows just how to palm these things whenever her mother looks away.

In the summer, too, business at the inn is slow. This week her mother has only one guest, a businessman from Chicago who checked in late last night, but she still insists on baking. It is a point of pride. Bozeman's is known for its baked goods, available to guests all day long. Today it's a new recipe from *Bon Appétit*, Carrot-Zucchini Muffins with Pecan-Coconut Streusel. "He works for some development company," her mother says as she slides a knife around each cup of the tin. "Bauder, his name is. They're looking for a ski resort to invest in. He said they're looking all over Vermont. Remodeling, a big advertising campaign, the works."

She pushes one of the muffins towards Elizabeth. "Here, taste this. Tell me if it's good." The tips of her first two fingers dance against the countertop as Elizabeth breaks off a chunk and places it in her mouth. "Imagine what that would do for Clayton. For us. How many more people would come in."

To Elizabeth the muffin tastes bitter, crumbling like wet sand. But she knows it's just her. "Mmm," she says, and smiles around the mouthful of mush. "Great recipe, Mom."

Her mother takes the empty tin to the sink and Elizabeth, perched on a stool at the counter, spits into a napkin and balls it up in her fist. "We need something like that," her mother is saying. "That kind of a boost. Your father was always saying so. If they decide to build up Pine Mountain –" She stops and opens the pantry for plastic wrap, and while her back is turned Elizabeth slips a spoonful of cornstarch into her mouth.

The frills on her mother's flowered apron wobble as she bundles Saran Wrap around each streuseled muffin. Elizabeth wants to reply but if she speaks a fine mist of starch will waft from her lips like a smoke signal. Instead she enjoys the softness of the dissolving starch, the delicate taste as she flattens the clumps against her palate.

"Let's hope for the best," her mother says finally. "He's here until Friday. Let's just show him the best side of Clayton. And Bozeman's." She turns. "Elizabeth, honey, you're so quiet. Is something wrong?"

Elizabeth swallows the starch, now turned to slurry in her mouth.

"No."

Her mother wipes her hands on her apron, a shred of plastic wrap clinging to her wrist. Then she turns back to the muffins and begins to place them into a ribboned wicker basket. "I just hate to see you looking so blue, honey," she says. Then: "Is it a boy?"

Elizabeth says nothing, licks starch off the ridges of her teeth.

"No, Mom," she says. "No, it isn't a boy."

* * *

Monday afternoons her mother tends the front garden, watering the marigolds, pulling crabgrass from around the sign that reads *Bozeman's: A Family Inn.* She won't change the name, even though for five years, since Elizabeth's father died, it's been just a family of two. "It's better for business," she always says.

Elizabeth goes for a run while her mother works. She jogs down into the town, where most of the kids from school live; she circles the high school itself, its parking lot empty, its fields dry and brown. On the way back she takes the long way, through the west side of Clayton, down the leafy street where she knows Jessica lives.

Last year, Jessica sat next to her in health class. When the teacher assigned them as project partners – alphabetically, Bozeman-Butler – Jessica didn't complain about getting the new girl who'd just transferred up two grades. Like everyone else in class, Jessica is older, but she smiles at Elizabeth, and tells jokes that make everyone, even the teachers, laugh. Once Jessica lent her a purple pen and instead of taking notes on the four food groups, Elizabeth placed the chewed cap in her mouth, fitting her teeth into the grooves Jessica had made. Jessica is seventeen and will be going to college in a year. So will Elizabeth, but that fact does not seem real.

When she thinks of Jessica, this is what she remembers:

Last October, picture day. In the bathroom girls shadow eyelids and mascara lashes. Elizabeth stands pigeon-toed in the corner by the sinks, and Jessica turns to her and smiles.

"Forgot your makeup?" she says. "Here, use mine." And she hands over a slim black tube of lipstick. Elizabeth has never done this before but she turns to the mirror, glides the stick across her lips, smudges the stain by pressing her lips together the way her mother does when she's angry.

"Thanks," she says and hands it back. In the mirror her reddened smile and Jessica's are identical. She licks the corner of her lips and tastes dark summer plums.

But the pictures come out badly. In each shot her eyes are some-where else – her lap, her hands, to the side of the frame, as if her attention lay just outside the picture, or as if she heard the footsteps of someone sensing something illicit. On the way home she rips the photos into shreds and places them, scrap by scrap, into her mouth, until the envelope is empty and the roof of her mouth is shriveled from the bitter developer.

The next week she'd slipped her hand into Jessica's bag and palmed the lipstick. That evening, at home, she'd locked her door before sliding the tube from her jeans pocket. She lifted the lid, admired the smooth, perfectly angled tip of the stick, the sharp sliced-off edges where the makeup rose to a point. It was too beautiful, too sculpted to bite. She swiveled the base and watched the lipstick emerge and withdraw like a waxy red tongue.

Today, as she runs past the house, she looks for Jessica, but there's no one there. Only a sprinkler on the front lawn, the fan of water waving back and forth, the edges of the spray rattling against the siding of the house, the grass a lush emerald.

When she comes home, her mother is sitting at the front desk with her head bent over the laptop screen. Elizabeth can't see the yellow and blue of the spreadsheet, but she knows what her mother is looking at. It's the thirtieth, and she's totaling up the month's earnings and expenditures, tapping a pencil along the row of numbers, the fingers of the other hand counting out the lines. Though she's done this for the past five years, Elizabeth's father was the one good with finances, and without him, the ledger grows unkempt. But lately there are fewer figures each month to total, and her mother's shoulders bow like overweighted shelves as she adds and re-adds.

Elizabeth goes upstairs to change. Her room is at the top of the inn – the servant's room before her parents bought and converted the mansion – but she likes its privacy, likes that she can look all the way down the curving road to the town spread out at the bottom of the hill like a map. It is the only room in the inn not decorated by her mother, the only room with no chintz and no antiques. The year before he died, Elizabeth's father painted the walls pale blue for his daughter; standing on the stepladder, he painted stars on the sloped ceiling with glow-in-the-dark paint. She's outgrown them now but leaves them up, because at night when she looks up to see the perfect five-pointed blotches, the comets in carefully tapering arcs, they remind her that she is no longer a child.

* * *

She doesn't meet the businessman until the next day. In the afternoon, while her mother is at the supermarket, Elizabeth puts on nice clothes and sits at the table they call the reception desk. At school she wears dark colors: navy, charcoal, maroon. Dressed like that, it's easier to blend with the sedate plastic chairs in the cafeteria, or the muted spines on the library shelves. But at reception her mother likes her to dress like she's going to church, though they haven't gone in years. She sits down in the Queen Anne armchair with a crossword puzzle book. Each time she fills in a word she tears a scrap from the answer pages and pops it into her mouth. The longer the word, the bigger the scrap. *Niche* earns a piece the size of her thumbnail; *zwieback* a piece the size of a cracker. She loves these afternoons, when no one is around and she can savor the chalky flavor.

At five she hears the town clock striking. Every day the bells play a different song, always painfully slow, but the tourists, when they are there, adore it. Today it's the Beatles, "Hey Jude." She reads "fleeting, transitory," writes *evanescent*, tears a last strip of paper and nibbles its edges. Her mother will be home soon. She's about to put it into her mouth endwise, like a piece of gum, when the businessman comes in. Elizabeth slides the paper between her fingers as he smiles, showing his teeth. He's maybe forty, but not bad looking, clean-shaven and dark-haired. Even before he leans in close to say hello she can smell his cologne, musky and damp.

"You must be Elizabeth," he says. "It's a pleasure to meet you."

When he speaks to her he stands so near that all she can see are the small things about him: the creases in the folds of his shirt; the pores on his cheek; how his hands are pale, like cheese. She has the urge to slide her chair backwards.

"You're holding down the fort?" he says, sitting on the edge of the table and unwrapping a muffin from the basket. "I hear you're going off to college soon." When she doesn't reply he asks, "Your mother runs this whole inn herself?"

She doesn't like the way he eats the muffin, breaking pieces off and pressing them between his finger and thumb before pushing them between his lips. So she nods and says only, "Since my father died." With the side of her hand she wipes the crumbs he's made off the table.

"I'm sorry," he says, and he seems to mean it. She feels his eyes rest on her, heavy as marbles.

"Are you having a nice stay in Clayton?" she says.

"It's a nice town," he says. "Nice scenery. Nice people. Could do with more business. I bet you could, too." She nods. "Well," he says, "maybe we can do something about that."

Elizabeth's mother comes in with a bag of groceries in each hand.

"Oh, Mr. Bauder," she says. "I see you've met Elizabeth. I hope she's being helpful."

"You have a very charming daughter, Mrs. Bozeman," he says. "We were just talking about Clayton and whether we could get more people to your lovely town." He stands up and gives her mother a smile, but this time his lips stay closed. "I've got to wash up before my dinner meeting. It was lovely meeting you, Elizabeth."

He goes into the front hall and Elizabeth hears his footsteps on the stairs. Her mother takes the bags into the kitchen.

"Such a nice man," she says. "Chicken for dinner, is that all right with you?"

Elizabeth waits until she hears the sizzle of oil in a hot pan before she uncurls the strip of crossword puzzle from her fingers. It holds its shape, like a fancy butter cookie. As she touches her tongue to it the businessman emerges from the front hall. She can't remember being caught before, not even when she was a child, and with her thumb she thrusts the entire curl of paper into her mouth. But she can tell by the way he pauses in the doorway that he's seen.

"Did I leave my pen?" he says. He scans the desk, then pats his pants pocket. "Ah. Here it is." He smiles at her, too broadly. She tucks the paper behind her molar, the way she sometimes does in class, and tries to smile back. When he leaves she fishes it out and finds it has gone soft as oatmeal.

* * *

Wednesday morning she'd like to run again, but this is her mother's busy day: farmer's market and antique fair. Elizabeth puts on a skirt, a flowered blouse. It's the kind of blouse Jessica might wear, and on impulse she takes Jessica's lipstick from the back of the underwear drawer. She hasn't used it much since taking it, so the tube is almost new. The maroon just matches the centers of flowers and she colors her lips carefully, outlining the edges with the tip before filling in the center with two broad swipes. She's sitting at reception again when the businessman arrives in midafternoon.

"Here again?" he says. He unwraps today's offering, double-chocolate-chunk cookies. "How come you're not out with your boyfriend on a nice day like this?"

"I don't have a boyfriend."

"What? A girl as pretty as you with no boyfriend?" He swallows a bit of cookie and reaches across and squeezes her hand. "Don't worry, Elizabeth. Do you want to hear my theory about boys?"

What she wants is to pull her hand back, but he's holding it tight and when she tugs just a little he doesn't loosen his grip. Instead she studies the guest register where his name is signed in green pen: Jack D. Bauder, Chicago, Illinois.

"Ever been to a party," he says, "where there's a bottle of soda sitting out on the table? That's what girls are like. Everyone just mills around looking at that soda, but no one wants to open it. But once the bottle's opened, everyone wants a cup. That's what boys are like. Meet one and they'll all come running." He lets go of her hand, crumples the plastic wrap and sets it on the table. She looks at him out of the corner of her eye, but she can't make out if he's smiling or serious.

"I've got another dinner meeting. Tell your mother her cookies are delicious." He winks at her and leaves. When he's gone Elizabeth rubs the back of her hand against her jeans. The ball of Saran Wrap slowly uncurls itself, its sound almost inaudible in the silent room.

* * *

At five-thirty, when her mother comes home with a shopping bag and a hurricane lamp, the businessman has left for his meeting. Elizabeth still hasn't thrown away the plastic from his cookie and her mother says, "Elizabeth! What a mess you've made. What would our guest say if he came in?"

"He came in a little while ago," Elizabeth says. "And then he went out again."

"Oh?" her mother says, going into the kitchen. Elizabeth follows her and leans on the counter while her mother takes tomatoes and basil and a bunch of daisies out of the bag.

"Just look at these tomatoes," her mother says. "Only four dollars for six. Did he say anything about the resort? Do you think they're going to invest?" She picks up the lamp she's bought and rubs at a speck on its base.

Elizabeth hesitates. "He didn't say anything," she says, and begins to shred the edge of the paper bag into pale brown fringe.

Her mother frowns. "I hope you were polite," she says.

"Of course I was." Elizabeth rips off two strips of bag and twists them around her fingertips. When she looks up, she's surprised to see her mother watching.

"What are you doing there?"

"Nothing," Elizabeth says. "Just playing around." She smiles cautiously at her mother and the milk-colored lamp, slides the curls of paper down her fingers like rings.

"I thought the lamp would look good in the green room," her mother says. She frowns again, then sets the lamp down and takes her wallet out of her purse.

"Why don't you go into town tomorrow and buy yourself a magazine," she says, putting a bill on the table. "Just a little something to cheer you up. You've been a big help to me this week."

"Okay," says Elizabeth. Under the edge of the counter, she pulls the brown paper from her hands and rolls it like a cigarette, and when her mother goes to put the lamp in its new place and the daisies in the businessman's room, she places the twist between her teeth and chews. The taste, like wheat, flowers on her tongue.

* * *

The next afternoon she goes into town as her mother suggested. But instead of walking to the drugstore, she heads to the café. She's not hungry, but her mother's ten-dollar bill is tucked in her jeans pocket, and she knows Jessica works there in the summer.

It's past lunch so the café is empty, and she sits by the window fingering the edges of the bill, resists the urge to smell it. She has never eaten money and wonders what it would be like. Crisp, she thinks, like lettuce, and probably salty from the grime of many palms. But she will not allow herself to try. This money, she thinks, is for normal use. And Jessica comes over, leans on Elizabeth's table.

"Hey there," she says. "Having a good summer? Nice blouse." Elizabeth's face goes warm, and all she can manage is "Thanks. Yeah. Can I have some ice cream?"

Jessica looks around. "My manager's out. Tell you what, it's on the house." She goes into the kitchen and comes back with two frosted bowls, sits down across the table. "God, it's hot. And it's so dead around here. No one's been in all day."

Elizabeth watches her spoon rocky road into her mouth. Jessica isn't wearing makeup today, and her lips are pale, only a little darker than her skin. Elizabeth says what she knows people always say. "How's your summer been?"

Jessica makes a face. "Work, work, work. And my dad thinks I should be studying for the SAT already. It's barely August." She licks coffee-colored cream from her spoon and tucks a wisp of hair behind her ear. "Your mom have anybody staying at the inn?"

"Just this weird guy," Elizabeth says. "This businessman from Chicago who's always trying to talk to me about boys."

Jessica laughs. "Creepy," she says. "What is it with old men like that? As if all we think about is boyfriends." She scoops a chunk of chocolate and looks Elizabeth in the eye and smiles with one side of her mouth. "Boys. Who needs them, right?"

As they sit there together, Elizabeth wants to tell Jessica everything that has ever happened to her: how she broke her arm sailing from a swing in sixth grade; the way her hands shook when the teacher made them partners; how she feels like God lying awake when the inn is full, sensing the people sleeping beneath her floorboards. More: the crunch of the first piece of chalk she ever ate, in kindergarten; the delicate flavor of plaster, tangy as sourdough bread; the way paper wilts, then congeals, in your mouth. She wants to pour her whole life into Jessica's ear; she wants to touch her tongue to Jessica's cheek and taste the fine down that glistens there like powder. And she reaches out and takes Jessica's hand.

Jessica's fingers are cold and Elizabeth wipes a smudge of chocolate from one glassy red-lacquered nail. Then Jessica draws her hand away, quickly, and Elizabeth sees that her eyes are wide and unblinking and won't meet hers.

"I've got to get back to work," Jessica says. She scoops up the bowls, one in each hand, and disappears into the kitchen. The kitchen door swings behind her, wildly at first and then less and less until Elizabeth isn't sure if it's still moving at all.

She leaves the whole ten-dollar bill on the table, even though she hasn't even tasted the ice cream, as if in exchange for amnesia, or at least a willful forgetting.

* * *

The businessman doesn't say anything when she comes into the sitting room, but he puts down the paper he's reading. She knows he's seen her face, her unlipsticked lips, the angry red smear where she's wiped her mouth on the back of her hand. On the coffee table is a new flower arrangement, tulips from the garden: her mother's afternoon occupation.

He's brought her a box of chocolate cordials, gold-wrapped and ribboned. "As a thank-you," he says. "For your hospitality. The job's done – I'll be leaving tomorrow."

She wants to tell him, "I don't like chocolate." *Of course you do,* she thinks. *Everybody likes chocolate.* The smell of the candy under her nose makes her dizzy. But he's so eager, the box tilted towards her on his palm, his eyes trained on her face like lights, studying its curves and planes. Even without looking she can feel that gaze, the weight of it on her cheek, how anxious he is to please. She smiles at him, runs her fingers along the tops of the chocolates, traces the molded swirls as her eyes rise to meet his. Then she lifts a piece and places it, whole, into her mouth, where it sits unmelting on her tongue.

"See?" he says. "Isn't it good?"

Her teeth break the shell of the candy and liquid, thick and choking, floods her mouth. Her throat burns, but she smiles as she swallows the whole mess without chewing again.

"Delicious," she says, and wipes the sticky syrup from the corner of her lips.

"You know what I could really go for?" he asks. He leans against the table, his hand almost touching hers. "A cup of coffee."

Elizabeth knows that the coffee pot is empty, that her mother has just gone out and won't be back until dinner. She looks up at him, puts her hand atop his and says, "I'll bring it up to your room."

From TV, and movies, she has an idea of what comes next. So she is not surprised when, as she sets the cup and plate on the desk, he guides her to sit on the corner of the bed and rubs her shoulders. She is not surprised as he strokes her hair, coaxes off her clothes. And she lets him. What she does not expect is the awkwardness of her body, which does not know how to bend, and the heaviness of his hands on her skin. And the taste of him: damp and sharp, like meat gone just sour. But she keeps her eyes open, banishing thoughts of soft, cold palms. She smiles as he hovers above her, as if this is what she truly wants.

Afterwards, he lies on his back with his eyes closed, half-covered by the sheet. She touches her toes to the wood floor and begins to pull on her clothes. When she is finished she turns around to find him watching her.

"You're leaving tomorrow, aren't you?" she asks.

"Yes." There is a long silence as she pulls the laces of her tennis shoes tight. "You're a good kid, you know that?" he says at last.

And because there is nothing else to say to this: "Yeah," she says, "I know."

She stays in her own room the rest of the day, telling her mother she isn't hungry at dinner, feigning sleep when her mother comes to check on her before bed. Lying in the dark, studying the stars that still glow faintly on the peaked ceiling above, she feels like she's under water.

* * *

Friday morning she sleeps late and when she wakes it's noon and he's checked out, gone.

"Elizabeth," her mother says when she comes downstairs. "What's the matter with you? Were you going to sleep all day?"

When she goes to clean his room, she locks the door. She ties back the curtains and peels the bedspread back. She doesn't know what she expects to see. Blood, maybe, like in the books she's read. Or something subtler, imprints of their bodies pressed into the linen, some marker of what had happened there. But the sheets are still the same off-white as always, barely even wrinkled.

Elizabeth strips the sheets from the bed and the cases from the pillows, bundling them in her arms. As she lifts them she thinks she smells him deep in the weave of the fabric: part cologne, part sweat. But when she sniffs again, the smell is gone, and she tosses the sheets into the laundry basket and begins to sweep. As she pushes the chair back into place she notices a business card fallen to the floor, almost hidden behind the desk leg.

It's thick and almost coarse, a pale creamy gold and crisp at the corners. At the top are the logo and address of a company, and beneath, his name and a phone number in glossy black lettering. She pivots the card between her fingers, watching his name flick in and out of view like an old movie: Jack D. Bauder. Jack D. Bauder.

She rips off a corner, leaving the lettering intact, and places it into her mouth.

The paper is tender, almost melting on her tongue, tasting of the dry heat of summer and the sour of lemonade. Fantasies hover like spiderwebs in the morning light. She imagines catching a train to Chicago, beginning a new life at the green address in the register. A life where chalk was for writing, paper for writing on, plaster for building walls on which to hang photographs of herself and the businessman, or a man just like him. A life where she would never slide magazine pages up her sleeve or lick dust from her fingers, where she would eat ice cream without remembering red-lacquered nails and eyes that slid away, where she would sit at a table and eat cornflakes in milk and would not think, as the cereal softened, of cardboard grown tender in the rain.

Then, almost before she knows it, she has eaten the whole card, and there is nothing but sunlight in her hands.

Shao Wang

ONE VOTED NO

– Inspired by the real event in a village in East China

Widow Zhang wished that she had never been widowed. All her family's trouble could be traced back to the death of her husband four decades ago – she realized this on the morning after a historic election in East China Village. When she was walking back from her Tai Chi session in the small village park, Liu Ping, the newly elected leader of the village, was chatting amicably with her neighbor. As soon as he saw Widow Zhang, Liu Ping closed his eyes, turned his back to her, and walked away.

Under normal circumstances, Widow Zhang would have just shaken her head and continued with her daily routine of gulping down a big bowl of noodle soup, eating the whites of two boiled eggs, and sipping a small glass of donkey penis wine. She didn't care that this wine was some kind of an elixir for men. Like everyone in the village, she followed Old Party Secretary Lao Liu's diet religiously and believed in its supreme benefits, for Lao Liu could never be wrong. He was still as strong as a tiger – according to his voluptuous secretary – which was a blessing to the citizens of East China Village.

Shao Wang's stories have appeared in *Zyzzyva*.

Lao Liu had single-handedly led the once poor village to become the richest one in Asia. This narrow strip of once barren marshland along the Yangtze River was now the headquarters of four giant corporations – one of which was listed on the Hong Kong Stock Exchange – and sixty companies. In 1999, a national newspaper reported that every one of the villagers earned more money than the U.S. President Bill Clinton did. As a widow with a disabled daughter, Widow Zhang owned shares of all of the four corporations, which were worth well over a million dollars in paper value. She collected a stipend of about 200 dollars a month, and lived with her daughter's family in a three-story American-style house with a swimming pool, which she used as a fish pond.

Widow Zhang's son-in-law was a foreman in a textile factory and her daughter, who had a crippled arm, was an accountant for a local tourist agency. Even though it was Sunday, they both were at work, for the only holidays in East China Village were two days during the Chinese New Year. Widow Zhang, a retired kindergarten teacher, had a lot of time on her hands, and perhaps that was the source of her trouble. She just couldn't stop thinking about why the new Party Secretary pretended that he hadn't seen her. She knew very well the reason: it was because she had voted against him the night before during the most important election in East China Village's history.

She cast the only "No" vote, along with an attempted abstention, in what would have been a unanimous election that passed the torch from a great father to a capable son. She could still hear the loud gasp in the hushed election room when her little pebble was dropped into the almost empty blue bowl next to the white bowl, which was piled high with stones. For a moment, the air seemed to have left the room; then, explosions of flash bulbs engulfed her as reporters shot pictures of her, the brave lone dissenter, and the symbol of Chinese democracy.

It was a terrible act that she had no way of avoiding, for she had been entrusted by Liu Ping's father, Lao Liu, to do so, in order to save the legitimacy of this election, and she knew perfectly well that she owed Lao Liu her allegiance, and understood why she was selected to cast the only dissenting vote, because her late husband was, for a brief period, the Party Secretary of this village and everyone knew that he used to follow the order and persecute Lao Liu at the beginning of the Cultural Revolution.

Yet, like everyone else in this village, Widow Zhang adored Lao Liu and prayed to Chairman Mao's spirit for Lao Liu to stay in office until his death, for she had personally benefited from Lao Liu's generosity and his commitment to the welfare of East China Village. And like everyone else in the village, when she heard the news that Lao Liu was considering retirement three weeks ago, Widow Zhang was shocked. Lao Liu had said that he would like to work until he was ninety years old and then spend his last ten years enjoying his life until he was "one hundred years old," which is the Chinese euphemism for death. Yet, he was only eighty years old now, still as robust as anyone half his age, and worked sixteen hours a day, every day of the year.

But unlike everyone else in the village, Widow Zhang decided to do something about it. She now spent much of her time in a retiree center called the "Second Youth Center" playing mahjong, watching TV, movies, and performances by local artists, and volunteering in a kindergarten with her fellow retirees. They got a free lunch every day, prepared by a chef hired from Sichuan Province. Every Chinese New Year, she received a bonus from Lao Liu based on how many grandchildren she had – she had two, and wished she had had eight, so that her reward would be quadrupled!

She washed her face carefully and put on some makeup to cover the age spots on her cheeks. At seventy-one, she looked younger than her age and healthy. She had a rosy face with deep wrinkles and a drooping mouth, but she still had clear eyes and strong teeth – thanks to the diligent doctor the village had hired from Hunan. She combed her hair, dyed jet black and piled it into a bun on top of her head. Through the window, she watched international and domestic tourists walk along the long Dragon Corridor that snaked around the village. The visitors' eyes grew wide as they stared at the Mercedes and Volvos parked in some of the driveways.

A village in a developing country was always associated with half-filled rice bowls, leaking roofs, mud walls, and back-breaking field work. Those conditions no longer applied to East China Village. This place was a paradise that Lao Tzu or Confucius could not have dreamed up.

Thirty years ago, the villagers ate tree bark and grass to fill their empty stomachs.

Twenty years ago, the villagers could only afford to buy meat once a month.

Ten years ago, the villagers were content to ride their new Phoenix bicycles to work.

And today . . .

Who would have imagined that Chinese farmers here live in new, three-thousand-square-foot houses with private swimming pools, and free access to community gym, tennis court and basketball court? Who would have believed that each family could own a car and every one was well-fed, healthy, and fully educated? Who would have dreamed that, instead of using outhouses where pigs would lick their asses clean, the villagers were now accustomed to marble toilets with automatic water sprayers, temperature control, and blow dryers attached to the seat so that toilet paper became obsolete? (Widow Zhang still did it the old way with the paper, though.) And who would have believed that this was simply the masterwork of one person, the great savior of East China Village, the venerable, and almost divine Old Party Secretary?

Now he was thinking of stepping aside!

What would happen to the villagers? What would happen to their houses, their cars, their stock shares, and their luxury retirement center? Most important, what would happen to their children and their grandchildren?

Widow Zhang felt an added responsibility, for she was the only party committee member in the village that was over sixty-five years old, except for the Old Party Secretary himself. She represented the senior citizens on the fifty-member committee, half of which was populated by Lao Liu's relatives, including his five sons and the son-in-law of his only daughter. She was sure that they wouldn't let him resign, and they alone could reject the proposal. She believed that the Old Party Secretary was just testing the waters, like smart Chinese emperors had done for centuries to check who was really loyal to him in order to cleanse the court of potential enemies before it was too late.

So this was the time for her to express her gratitude and to once again atone for what her late husband had done to Lao Liu during the Cultural Revolution – he once tortured Lao Liu, trying to force a confession from him.

She called the Old Party Secretary's office. His young secretary told her that Lao Liu was in neighboring Plum Village discussing a possible merger of the two villages. Believing that she should be the first one to speak out, Widow Zhang trudged toward the village gate and was about to catch a bus to Plum Village when two guards stopped her by the golden-arched gate. She suddenly remembered that she didn't have permission to leave the village compound and the guards, though they knew her well, would not budge. She turned around and decided that she should talk to Lao Liu in the evening before the daily party committee meeting so that she could be one step ahead of the others.

She returned to the Second Youth Center and resumed playing mahjong with her friends. She lost a lot that day, since her mind was not on the game – Lao Liu had specifically allowed the seniors to gamble with a limit of 20 yuan per day per person to keep their brains busy, but forbidden young people from playing the game and wasting their precious time and energy. However, Widow Zhang knew that many young people gambled a bit with their parents and neighbors at home.

At 6:00 pm, she called Lao Liu again and was told that he wouldn't be back until 6:30 pm, which was his TV time – Lao Liu got many ideas from watching the daily news programs. His most famous business initiative was to predict correctly that there would be a steel shortage when the government announced its new development program in the early 1980s. The village made a killing by hoarding iron, steel, and coal.

Widow Zhang found herself in a dilemma. She ate her food by the window, musing. Lao Liu's TV time was regarded as the most sacred of his day. Nobody was allowed to interrupt him while he watched the news, unless there was an emergency. At 7:00 pm, he would saunter across the street to lead the daily party committee meeting, and would listen to reports of the managers' activities and give new directives, based on the day's top news.

East China Village was famous for meetings and the managers were supposed to work sixteen hours a day. Widow Zhang was the only one in the meeting that enjoyed the luxury of retirement, though she provided her inputs into the decision-making process, on behalf of the old folks. She was sure that she would be given a chance to speak out against Lao Liu's retirement at the meeting, but if she visited his house first and told him in his face, the old man would appreciate it, despite the disruption of his daily routine. They had known each other for a long time, and once many, many years ago, they were clandestine lovers, after the sudden death of her husband in a traffic accident. Lao Liu knew the secrets of every old folk in the village; unlike most of his children, who had no idea about their brief liaison and their joint past. She was sure that with Lao Liu gone, the old folks' benefits would be dramatically cut. So when the clock struck 6:30, Widow Zhang took a deep breath, straightened her back, pulled open the door, and marched bravely towards Lao Liu's house.

Lao Liu's wife had passed away a few years back. He lived alone in the old part of the village. His was the shabbiest house in East China Village. The old man insisted on living there until everyone in the village had been moved to new houses. "Even an emperor could only occupy one bed at a time and eat no more than his share of the food," Lao Liu liked to say. It was a two-story red brick house. From outside, it looked no different from the houses in the surrounding villages, but compared with Zhang's American-style house, it was a cave.

The door was wide open, as always. After she yelled a "hello," Widow Zhang barged in. She walked across the dining room and pushed open the door to the living room. As expected, Lao Liu was sitting on his sofa, his eyes glued to the TV, on which showed news footage of yet another tycoon, listed as one of the top ten richest men in China by the annoying Forbes magazine, being arrested for tax evasion.

"Old Secretary," Widow Zhang called out.

Lao Liu's whole body jutted forward as if he were being sucked into the TV screen. All of a sudden, he hit his thigh and shouted, "That bastard deserves a bullet!"

"Old Secretary." Widow Zhang tried calling him again.

There was a moment of silence. In the dim light, Widow Zhang thought she saw a bulging vein on Lao Liu's temple pop out and his neck expand until it almost exploded. She shivered, knowing that Lao Liu must be upset. "Don't you ever interrupt my – " Lao Liu stopped in his tracks. He turned to see Widow Zhang. A reluctant smile spread on his face. Widow Zhang sighed with relief. At least, he still remembered their joint history.

Lao Liu barked an order and his young secretary scurried in from a room in the back. Widow Zhang wondered why the woman was in Lao Liu's bedroom – the room where they made love eons ago. She heard Lao Liu ask his secretary to watch the rest of the news and to brief him on it later. Then he waved his hand, and the young woman returned to the room, closing the door behind her.

Widow Zhang wondered if the bedroom had now been converted into his private study. She suddenly remembered unhappily that Lao Liu's secretary used to be a middle school teacher. She heard Lao Liu cough, so she asked, "Lao Liu, I heard you are going to retire; is it true?"

Lao Liu stood up and walked to the door. He made sure that it was locked. He sat next to Widow Zhang on the sofa. In a whisper, he said, "You came at the right time. I was thinking about you this evening."

Widow Zhang squirmed in her seat. She felt Lao Liu's thigh uncomfortably pressed against hers; she could even smell the familiar cigarettes on his breath. Her heart fluttered. Not that she had never sat so close to him, but that was long ago, and seemed to have been in a different life.

"I'm proposing to retire this evening."

"Why? You said you would lead us until you were eighty-five . . ."

"I realize now that eighty-five is too late. I need to select a successor and train him during the first several years. So, I've decided this is the best time to retire. Eighty years old is no longer young, Widow Zhang."

Widow Zhang turned to study the deep creases on his rugged face and the varicose veins on his arms. She wondered if this was the same person with whom she had been madly in love forty years ago. She was young, newly widowed, and he had been relieved of his job as the County Director for following the capitalist road. Back then he was a handsome middle-aged man. The hard muscles on his chest and those powerful hands – her heart trembled as she looked at the loose skin on his neck.

"Who is going to be your successor?" Widow Zhang asked.

Lao Liu pondered for a moment and asked, "Who do you think should succeed me?"

A dangerous question, Widow Zhang thought. If she picked the wrong horse and if someone ever leaked the contents of this conversation out, her family could be in trouble. Her eyes stared at the door to the bedroom.

Lao Liu chuckled. "Nobody will hear us."

Widow Zhang thought about Lao Liu's children. They were named after Chinese communist leaders: Mao Ze Dong, Zhu De, Zhou En Lai and Deng Xiao Ping. His oldest son, Liu Dong, was the President of the Steel Group, the largest entity in East China Village. He was wise and cautious, but he was also a bit too old, in his sixties. Liu De, his second son, the head of the Logistics Group, was well-educated, but had a hot temper. He was not liked by the villagers. His third son Liu Lai was in charge of the Food Group, which exported eel fish to Japan and canned mushrooms to the U.S. He was quiet and almost passive, so he was not the right choice. Liu Ping, the youngest son, used to be in the army. He was recently promoted to lead the fourth group, which mainly engaged in joint product development leveraging on East China Village's popular brand name, such as East China Village Whisky, East China Village Cigarettes, East China Village Beat-the-Viagras for men and women, and East China Village Slim Extreme Fast. His group was the most profitable. Then there was his son-in-law, who had a college degree and who was in charge of public relations.

The five men basically controlled every aspect of East China Village. She reminded herself again to be careful with her recommendations. So she asked, "Lao Liu, what's your choice?"

"What do you think about Liu Ping?"

Widow Zhang's heart sank. His youngest son had traveled to many places in China. He could be a good choice, but Widow Zhang had heard rumors that he also inherited his father's weakness for women. In fact, it was whispered in the village that he flirted with Lao Liu's young secretary, who at this very moment was right next door in Lao Liu's bedroom, supposedly watching the nightly news.

"Why?" she asked.

"He's my youngest child, the only one who still has fire in his belly." Lao Liu paused. Then he added, "If I want a captain to keep this ship sailing, I want him to be at the helm for a long, long time."

Widow Zhang nodded. She had to agree that it was a good idea. Young and robust, Liu Ping was like his father in many ways. Besides, he was the only one in the family, perhaps in the world, who knew of her short affair with Lao Liu, for Lao Liu used to take the little boy to her house for "poetry classes." However, she was not sure what the young man thought of their little tryst decades ago.

She remembered that the boy had drifted away briefly and enrolled in the army. When he returned, he married the woman Lao Liu had selected for him and then tried to help the poorest villages in western China. Rumor had it that he had fathered several children there.

Like father, like son. Widow Zhang eyed Lao Liu and wondered how he could still satisfy a woman at such an advanced age. She glanced nervously at the bedroom door. Widow Zhang couldn't even control her bladder now. She felt her face flush and her hands shiver at the thought.

"You don't like him?" Lao Liu frowned.

As a boy, Liu Ping recited the poems of Tang dynasty she had assigned him in the living room while she made love with his father in her bedroom. The boy must have been upset, being left alone to do his homework. Did Lao Liu think that she was worried about that? Certainly not – Widow Zhang knew that Lao Liu had at least one other secret affair after theirs. A man with his success, stamina, and intelligence was admired by many and fantasized about by half of the village women.

"Of course – of course, I adore him. He is the best choice, but I don't believe he is as good as you are."

"You know me better than anyone," Lao Liu patted her arm. His hand was cold and bony, no longer the warm, hungry talon that used to squeeze hot sensation into her swelling breast. She realized that he was slowly descending into the grave, just like her. They were all dying.

"If you insist, I will vote for him. Do you want me to nominate him?" she asked.

Lao Liu shook his head. "That's not a good idea. My other sons will hate you. I will nominate him, and I am sure that he will get a unanimous vote."

"I'm sure, too." Widow Zhang said quickly.

"But, I have a favor to ask of you," Lao Liu said, glancing at her sideways.

"What?"

"I want you to cast the only vote against him." Lao Liu scratched his head.

Widow Zhang almost jumped, saying violently, "NO!"

"You must do it," Lao Liu said. He explained that in another famous village down the Yangtze River, when the Old Party Secretary retired, he named his son to be his successor and the vote was unanimous. There was instant media uproar about a feudal family dynasty and a puppet party committee, which dared not dissent. He wanted Widow Zhang to show the world that their system was a truly democratic one where everyone could vote from his or her heart, just as Widow Zhang would do.

"But why me?" Widow Zhang cried. The vote would be open. There would be two bowls placed on a table set in the front of the voting place. One for "Yes" and the other for "No." She was sure that no one would dare to challenge Lao Liu's wishes, so she would be the only one and she knew why – her late husband, Lao Liu's rival, only briefly.

"No, I will not," she repeated.

They heard a knock on the door and Lao Liu's secretary called from inside the bedroom that the news program had just ended and they should go to the meeting.

The old man stood up and stroked Widow Zhang's lined face. "Don't argue with me, sweetheart. Do as I ask."

His soft voice instantly took Widow Zhang back forty years and she still remembered Lao Liu's hard muscles when she rested her head on his body. She could even recall the small beads of perspiration that rolled down his skin as his chest rose and fell, rose and fell, like a spent accordion. His heartbeat was the most beautiful music to her youthful ears. She knew that she had no choice. So she said, "But Liu Ping will hate me."

"He won't," Lao Liu waved his hand dismissively, "And it doesn't matter. As long as I am around, he can't touch you."

But what if you die? What if we all die and he takes it out on my daughter and my son-in-law? She wanted to ask; instead, she said meekly, "Please tell him that you asked me to do so."

Lao Liu grunted, as if to say yes.

The general election for the new Party Secretary of East China Village was held three weeks later in the mess hall. Reporters from across the country flocked there, along with some of their international colleagues. Lao Liu had stated publicly that he was following the example of China's paramount leader Deng Xiao Ping and was ready to retire. The party committee members were upset at first, and saddened when they realized that Lao Liu would not back down from his decision. Many of them sobbed fervently as if their own fathers had just passed away.

Lao Liu declared that he put Liu Ping's name on the ballot only because of his youth. There was no opposition, not even from Lao Liu's other sons. After an awkward silence, Lao Liu turned to ask his eldest son, Liu Dong, for his opinion. As expected, the eldest son immediately praised Lao Liu's wise decision, and the rest of the committee members followed suit, declaring that Liu Ping was the superb choice. The villagers stood in the back of the brightly lit mess hall with blank faces.

After Lao Liu nodded, his secretary brought out two big bowls, a blue one for "No" votes and a white for "Yes" votes, and fifty stones. She placed the bowls on the table and distributed the stones among the committee members. Lao Liu stood up and encouraged his committee members to exercise their democratic right and cast a vote for the villagers they represented. Then he put his stone in the white bowl.

Liu Dong threw a stone into the same bowl after his father, and there was a loud cracking sound. The villagers laughed. Liu De, the second son also expressed his support. Liu Lai, the third son, stood up and studied the two bowls. He turned to survey the committee members and gently placed his stone in the empty space between the two bowls.

There was commotion in the room, but Lao Liu coughed; after a moment, he said sharply. "Either vote yes or no. There's no third choice."

Liu Lai ignored his father and stormed out. Liu Ping bolted up, grabbed the stone, and threw it into the blue bowl. "Refusing to vote yes, means no to me," he said sternly, his eyes sweeping the rest of the committee members.

Widow Zhang's heart shuddered at Liu Ping's steely voice. She knew that Liu Lai was not on speaking terms with Liu Ping because rumor had it that Liu Ping had seduced Liu Lai's mistress, a retired local opera starlet. Liu Lai had also bragged that he was the smartest person in this family. In fact, licensing East China Village's name to make business profits was his idea. He was also the only person in the family that dared to argue with his father. He had a few supporters, who had for years called for a competitive election in the village.

Liu Ming, Lao Liu's son-in-law shuffled up to the table. Everyone now stared at him. Widow Zhang knew that Liu Ming, who had changed his last name after he married Liu's daughter, was a drinking buddy of Liu Lai. She watched with rising anticipation. Liu Ming dangled his stone in the air, and, for a moment was about to cast a "No" vote. Lao Liu suddenly stood up and walked to his side.

"Use your own judgment, Liu Ming," he said. "Vote from your heart."

Liu Ming's hand trembled, and as if by accident, the stone slipped out of his fingers and landed in the white bowl. Liu Ping smiled and exhaled with a long sigh.

After that, it was a breeze. Everyone voted "Yes." So the white bowl filled up quickly, and the blue one remained empty, except for that one annoying stone.

Widow Zhang waited until the last minute. She tried to get a signal from Lao Liu, but the retiring party secretary was busy talking with his eldest son. When she realized that everyone in the room was watching her, she crept towards the table. The flash bulbs blinded her for a moment.

She didn't know what to do. Now that there already was a "No" vote, perhaps hers was not necessary? She couldn't afford to offend any of the Lius. She knew that a wrong move could mean the destruction of her family.

Last week, when her friend was visiting her cousin, Widow Zhang asked her son-in-law to step in and play mahjong for an hour. It happened that Lao Liu's secretary came to her house to deliver an emergency meeting announcement and caught them red-handed. "Don't you know Lao Liu's rule that only seniors can play mahjong?" she asked harshly and left. Widow Zhang blamed herself for that mistake. Lao Liu had not come to her house since he had ended their affair, at her request, because the rumors had begun to haunt her. She was sure that his secretary had reported her transgression and knew that if Lao Liu had wanted to kick them out, he could easily have done so, because his word was law.

A year ago, Widow Zhang's old neighbor was caught selling handmade quilts at the county fair and she was driven out of her new house, her benefits were cut off and her shares in the village were relinquished. To avoid corruption there was a clear rule that any employee of East China Village could not have a second job. One day, her neighbor lived like a queen, and the next day, she was homeless. The poor woman begged at the village gate and blamed herself for the stupidity. She kept saying that she would never do it again.

Now, Widow Zhang was sure that if she voted the wrong way tonight, Lao Liu was going to remember the incident and the same tragedy would happen to her family. She looked to Lao Liu for a signal, but he ignored her. Worse, the old man stood up and pulled his eldest son to the window.

With no guidance, Widow Zhang decided that she should follow the predetermined route. She was about to cast her "No" vote when she heard a surprised murmur come from the audience. A hush followed. Everyone in the room was staring at her now and the flash bulbs froze her in a white haze. Her hand trembled. She heard a soft gurgle and turned to the left, only to see the dark stare of Liu Ping, who bit his lip and nodded, as if to say, "If you dare to do this, I will let you know how much this No vote will cost you."

Widow Zhang reckoned that Lao Liu shouldn't be worried about the appearance of an undemocratic process, since there was already a "No" vote. So she moved to the right and was about to drop the stone into the white bowl when she heard Lao Liu burst into a coughing spasm. She turned to the window and saw Lao Liu's face darken with rage. No one had ever opposed him unscathed. She was about to cry, not knowing what to do. Finally, she decided to follow Lao Liu's order, so her hand slowly shifted to the blue bowl.

Then again she peered at Liu Ping, who folded his arms and fixed her with an intense gaze. Her eyes stayed on his whitening knuckles. She trembled.

As if pulled by a mysterious power, the stone in her hand slipped and hit the edge of the white bowl, and mysteriously bounced and dropped into the blue bowl with a ding. "It's . . ." she stammered, hoping that someone in the mess hall could exonerate her mishap by pointing out that she had actually intended to vote "Yes." It was just an act of God, not of her own will.

"Widow Zhang, do you want to recast your vote?" She heard Liu Ping ask her.

She hesitated, her hand automatically reached out. Then she felt the icy stare of Lao Liu.

"No – no, that's okay," she said. "I'm a bit dizzy." She heard a chuckle in the crowd and was relieved that it was all over.

Lao Liu sauntered to the middle of the table and solemnly declared that there were 48 "Yes" votes and 2 "No" votes. Comrade Liu Ping was formally elected the Party Secretary of East China Village. Everyone gave Liu Ping a standing ovation. Widow Zhang applauded enthusiastically. After a few seconds, Liu Lai returned to the room and clapped his hands to show his consent of defeat and shook hands with Liu Ping. The camera flashed and clicked. To her horror, Widow Zhang thought she saw Liu Lai giving his little brother a conspiratorial wink.

Liu Ping then bowed to his father and promised that he would work extremely hard to carry the torch forward. He then walked down from the podium and shook hands with all the committee members in the room.

Widow Zhang found herself sweating and trembling when Liu Ping stood in front of her with the two reporters focusing their cameras on them. He seemed to be saying something, but his lips barely moved. He grabbed Widow Zhang's hand and squeezed it so hard that her knuckles cracked. She winced.

Liu Ping gave her a toothy smile and left.

One by one, the party committee members departed. Someone turned the lights off, leaving the dazed Widow Zhang alone in the mess hall, as if she were an invisible ghost. She regretted that she hadn't cast the "Yes" vote, because she was sure everyone would think that she was against the new Party Secretary. Then she convinced herself that Lao Liu would tell his son the truth, and Liu Ping would realize that she was trying to provide legitimacy to his election, just like his brother Liu Lai had done, and would forgive her, if not thank her.

The next day, Widow Zhang found her name and picture in the local and national newspapers. The commentators praised the election as open and fair. Reporters flocked to her door to interview her as if she were a heroine and the symbol of democracy in rural China.

Through his office, Liu Lai issued a statement saying that he supported his younger brother and always thought that he was very well qualified. He cast an abstaining vote to show his respect for his other brothers, and his father, since he was adamantly opposed to Lao Liu's early retirement. He believed that his father could live to be a hundred and twenty years old and, therefore, he should not retire until he was a hundred years old.

Lao Liu was absent for the first time in his life from the party committee meeting that evening and Liu Ping declared that his father had reaffirmed his intention to retire and had said that henceforth he would no longer attend any committee meetings. He would merely function as an advisor. If he had an important idea, he would ask his secretary, who now sat in for him, to deliver it to the committee. Liu Ping also announced that Lao Liu had given him the power to reorganize the leadership of the party committee so that he could get the most out of his management team.

With that said, he stated that he maintained his confidence in the existing managers and asked them to remain in their posts with a proposed salary increase of 500 percent. He said that he was also aware of the toll the hard work had taken on the villagers, especially the seniors. He had never realized how tired his father was until the day Lao

Liu told him that he was exhausted and wanted to have a rest. With respect to the old comrades who deserved a peaceful retirement, he proposed that the party committee members should retire before they reached seventy years old.

All eyes stared at Widow Zhang, since she was the only one in the room above the new age limit. Liu Dong, the new Party Secretary's eldest brother was sixty-four years old. The room was now quiet and everyone waited for Widow Zhang to make a rebuttal. She stood up and wrung her hands. "I – I am very grateful for the Party Secretary's concern about our health. I second the proposal."

Everyone followed Liu Ping's lead and applauded.

Widow Zhang's daughter and son-in-law were horrified when they heard the results of the election. They pestered her and asked why she voted the way she did. She could give no reason for her action. They urged her to explain to the authorities that she was confused on the election day and the stone slipped from her hand into the wrong bowl. She had intended to cast a yes. She should be given another chance. They reminded her that, unlike his father, Liu Ping had a small heart and a long memory.

Widow Zhang found herself standing in front of Lao Liu's house that evening, but she sensed that something was wrong, for there were no lights inside and the usual TV sounds had disappeared. The house was silent. She wondered if Lao Liu was on a trip or had already gone to bed.

All of a sudden, she heard glass shattering and Lao Liu's angry voice. He was crying.

Oh, poor man!

Widow Zhang stumbled into the house and saw Lao Liu standing in the middle of the dining room in his patched pajamas. He had never looked so old. His sparse hair was snow white; his beard soiled with drops of food and soy milk, and he smelled like dried fish. He slouched towards the door, as if his head was too heavy for his frail body. With his hands scratching the air, he looked disoriented.

A dim light streamed in from the TV room. She turned on the wall switch and the room became bright. Seeing blood dripping from his hand, she took out a handkerchief and wrapped it around his wound.

"What happened, Little Liu," she asked, not realizing that she was calling him by the name she used to call him when they were young.

"Motherfucker, I can't see my news – my TV broke, and the mechanic was supposed to arrive at 6:30."

Widow Zhang glanced at the old clock on the wall: it was 7:15. She wondered if the broken TV was a coincidence.

"Where is your secretary, Lao Liu?" she asked.

"That whore! Yesterday she said that Liu Ping asked her to do some work for him and never returned."

Widow Zhang helped Lao Liu into the TV room. He collapsed onto the sofa, panting. "They forget you as soon as you are of no use to them. That's why I never wanted to retire."

Widow Zhang found a thermos on the floor and poured some hot tea in a cup and asked, "Why did you?"

"My doctor said that I had a serious condition and needed surgery, so I was persuaded by Liu Ping to retire. Now, I suspect that the doctor must have been bribed by him." He stopped and gestured for Widow Zhang to sit next to him. She hesitated for a split second before she obliged. He wrapped his arm around her shoulder and sighed. "I hear that they drove you out of the party committee. Now, the two of us have been left out in the cold." He choked back the tears that dripped down his puffy face.

Widow Zhang fumbled for her handkerchief, then she realized that it was on Lao Liu's injured hand, so she wiped his eyes with the back of her hand. Tenderness swept her like ocean waves as she remembered the short, torrential love affair they had years ago – like a yellowed picture from another time. He was still the same vulnerable, lonely hero. On impulse, she leaned over and kissed the tears from his face.

Lao Liu froze; his hand brushed Widow Zhang's sagging breast. Reluctantly, he pushed her away and groaned, "Old lady, you are the only person I can trust now."

Widow Zhang was ashamed of her sudden show of affection. She stood up and straightened her shirt.

"Why don't you talk with Liu Ping?"

"He's cancelled the daily meeting and I can't find him and my other sons anywhere. They are always busy."

Widow Zhang's heart sank.

"So you never told Liu Ping about my vote?"

Lao Liu wiped his face and waved his rugged hand as if he were driving away a mosquito. "It's useless, the ingrate hates me, now I know that. Whatever I tell him will have the opposite effect."

"But – but what will happen to me – to my family?" Widow Zhang asked, almost in tears. "I won't survive if I am expelled from East China Village."

"Don't worry," Lao Liu said gallantly, pulling her down on the sofa. "I can protect you. Remember when you were first widowed with a little daughter, and the neighborhood hooligans tried to take advantage of you?"

Widow Zhang smiled. Of course, she remembered. She had been a beauty. Lustful single men swarmed outside her windows almost every evening. Lao Liu was then Little Liu, who had just been demoted from the position of County Director to the Party Secretary of East China Village. He was depressed and angry and lived alone – his wife refused to leave her better life in the county seat, Hua Yang City. When she begged him to intervene after she was almost raped one night, he took a rifle and shot the hooligan's ear off, and made sure that the whole village knew that she was under his protection – even though they were not close then because her late husband had opposed him. Their love affair began to blossom after he had settled down and re-established his authority in the village. By then, he would take his youngest son, Liu Ping, to her house for tutoring in classic poems . . . They even talked about getting married . . . but she begged off, because she knew that it was impossible for him to get a divorce and it would hurt his political future. Even then she was sure that he was not an ordinary man and that he would one day become very famous with his pictures in every newspaper in China – a prediction that eventually came true. Yet it took him another thirty years of struggle before East China Village became the richest village in the nation.

In the fervor of love, he almost quit his political career to become an average farmer so that he could live with her forever. But she reminded him that without power, he could neither protect himself nor her. The best thing he could do was to stay the boss of the village. He reluctantly consented and left her when his wife returned to the village with his other children. She had never remarried; and he had made sure that she lived comfortably. He even found a husband for her disabled daughter.

"Remember, you used to ask Liu Ping to stand outside reciting a long romantic Tang poem while we made love in the bedroom – what was that poem?" He tried to recall the words, but his memory had faded.

She tried to help him, but her brain was wrapped in dense fog. She only remembered it was about two birds and some trees. "I always felt that you were with me," Widow Zhang said. "It was worth all of my love to be with you back then."

"And all the years while I was having a great time running this village." Lao Liu wrapped his arm around Widow Zhang. "I am sorry, really sorry," he said.

Widow Zhang patted the back of his parched hand, "Don't be. I'm very happy now."

"Let's get married tomorrow," Lao Liu said.

"Now?" Widow Zhang turned to look at the octogenarian sitting next to her. She couldn't believe her ears.

"Why not? At least we can spend a few years openly together, not living like a couple of thieves. Marrying me could also provide protection for your family."

Widow Zhang hung her head.

Lao Liu propped her chin up and found that she was weeping.

"Why are you crying?"

"Do you know how many nights I have dreamed of this day, Lao Liu?" Widow Zhang covered her face with her hands. Lao Liu stared at the loose skin on her small, stick-thin arm.

"It's my fault. All this glory was for nothing. Look at me now!"

"Will your children approve of our marriage or will they call me a gold-digger?"

Lao Liu laughed. "What gold do I have? My bank account is smaller than that of most of the villagers here, and my house is a dump. Gold, you are my piece of gold! Even my secretary disappeared like a rat from a sinking ship, and you think I have gold? I don't need to worry about my reputation any more, and my vanity is gone. I only need a companion that I can trust. I don't need to listen to anyone but myself, so don't worry about gossip."

Widow Zhang stood up. "This is too fast. I have to talk with my daughter."

"Don't keep me waiting too long, old widow. I want us to have the most luxurious wedding ever seen in this village. I will invite the Premier of China to preside over our ceremony."

Widow Zhang knew he could do that. She felt that her legs were about to melt. She stumbled out of the house, trying to convince herself that she was not walking on clouds. She didn't know whether to cry or laugh.

The next morning, Widow Zhang combed her hair and took out her treasured red satin dress, which she reserved for the Chinese New Year. It took tremendous control to withhold the news of her wedding from her daughter and son-in-law. She decided to go back to make sure that Lao Liu really meant what he had said before she revealed the engagement to her family.

As she reached Lao Liu's house, she saw an ambulance and a crowd of people. Liu Ping was barking orders to his deputies. His face fell when he saw Widow Zhang. "What are you doing here, Old Widow?" he asked sharply.

"I'm meeting Lao Liu." She looked at the ground, embarrassed to be wearing her red dress.

Liu Ping said, "The old man dropped dead of a heart attack last night. Someone said you had stayed with him for a very long time." After a pause, Liu Ping asked, "What the fuck did you do? Teach him romantic poems?"

The bystanders laughed, but stopped when Liu Ping stared coldly at them.

Widow Zhang's face turned pale. She almost fainted. A neighbor caught her before she fell.

The funeral was grandiose. Officials from Beijing and the provincial capital came to pay their tribute to the model communist cadre. Everyone in the village attended it, except one person. The Vice-Premier in charge of agriculture delivered a short eulogy. Liu Ping, wearing a black band on his arm, presided over the ceremony. With tears in his eyes, he vowed to carry out the Old Party Secretary's unfinished business and make the village a sustainable communist Utopia. The day ended with a ten-course banquet and a bikini fashion show to entertain the VIP guests.

That night, someone found that Widow Zhang had hung herself in Lao Liu's house. When he heard the news from Lao Liu's former secretary, a half-drunk Liu Ping squeezed her swelling breast and sighed, "I've never thought that she had loved him so much that she would defy him and vote against me."

"I've never heard him talk about her," the secretary whispered.

"Do you know which Tang poem she had me memorize?" Liu Ping laughed, then he recited it in a high-pitched boy's voice:

> "If we ever go to heaven
> We shall be a pair of soaring birds
> If we ever go to underworld
> We shall be the roots that connect two trees . . ."

Michael Hawley

DIPTYCH

The way that she halts in the middle of the room, with the torque of her hips arrested mid-stride, Glover knows that something is wrong. The thirteen-year-old has just woken up and is sitting at the end of the bed in his underwear.

"What?" His eyes bat as if to clear the remnant of a cruelly pleasant dream.

She takes a step nearer, hugging his laundered clothes to her chest. She bends forward. Her long brown hair slides over her shoulders. "Your eye, Glover."

There is a wateriness in his right eye, a hovering discomfort – but only now that Winnie has pointed it out. She plops the stack of clothes on the bed and sweeps back her curtain of hair. "Don't touch *any*thing, Glover!"

Fluttering her hands, Winnie snaps from the room, slamming the door behind her. Glover sits perfectly still for a moment, his sandy hair in paralyzed contortions. He wonders if she did the same thing to Lucas, just barging in any old time.

Glover's last foster parents had pretty much let him alone. For

Michael Hawley's stories have appeared in *Southeast Review, Boston Review,* and *The New Yorker.*

almost two years, the binge-drinking Liptaks of Ozone Park had remained an agreeable mystery. Not so Winnie Ramos. In six weeks, he has come to know her precisely – the cold optimism and warm self-regard. She routinely compares him to her son, Lucas, her strapping, athletic and "respeckful" teenager who grew up to manage a car dealership somewhere north of Poughkeepsie.

Glover pulls on his jeans and consults the oval mirror on the bureau. The eye rises like a red planet. He leans close to examine it. A bullet of pus in the inside corner changes shape with each swipe of the lid. He feels a tug at the back of his stomach, like a loose suture pulling tight. He bends closer. The veins of the eye look swollen; their fingers clutch at the rose-tinted surface. He blinks, the bullet flattens. A thread of it, thin as spider's silk, is drawn up by his lashes.

"Don't touch it!" Winnie shrieks, thrusting in once more. Her gait slows as he turns from the mirror. Again he senses a change in her, a shift away. The red of the eye sears the distance between them. Raising the burnished buckler of her smile, Winnie resumes her advance. In her hand: a white, wet, steaming washcloth.

"Pinkeye is very contagious, Glover. Very catching. Sit."

Winnie sits, too – measuredly close – her denim skirt stiff against the bedspread. Dressed to meet her Watchtower friends for their daily Pioneering, she wears a khaki blazer and a powder blue cotton blouse.

"Do you know where you got it?" she asks him, a vapor of Listerine in the words.

"No."

Her index finger, wrapped in a corner of the washcloth, affixes itself to Glover's right cheek and pulls at the lower lid.

"Those video games at the corner, I expeck. Don't pull away!"

Glover, submitting, avails the eye to a thorough inspection. Winnie releases him. Her eyes sweep to the top of the bureau, where a photo of Lucas with his swim team had stood. As if remembering she had moved it to the dining room recently, her gaze retreats to the window. It stalls there, searching, it seems, for a reason to be there.

"Come," she says, rising. "And don't touch anything."

Glover squints against the blaring light and surfaces of the bathroom.

"I'm meeting Yolanda downstairs," says Winnie. She turns the spigot as hot as it will go. "Now remember, Glover. Wash your hands first, then your face, then your hands again. Then shower."

He watches her in the mirror of the medicine cabinet. She has to stand on her toes to reach the can of Lysol on top of the storage unit.

The eye turns to its own reflection. The rim of the upper lid tingles in the light; he can feel the pulse of blood under it. The veins on the eyeball form an intricate system of deltas around the iris. He lowers his hands to the running water, unable to look away.

"Glover? Call Dr. Rivera and make an appointment. Try for this morning. Tell him it's urgent. I'll leave his number on the table. *And*," she adds, her breasts jogging as she shakes the spray can, "I want you to scrub every inch of your room. Promise me."

Armed with the Lysol, she marches down the hall. She prowls the apartment, spritzing doorknobs and light switches. She goes in his room and fogs it down good. He pictures her stalking around the bed, searching out evil deposits on the pillow case – the faded trails of wanton dreams.

Winnie had removed the photo for a reason. She had popped in one morning – again unannounced – with all the radiance of Jehovah's Anointed. He had whipped the sheet over what he'd been doing, his eyes caught to hers. Never had he seen a face change so thoroughly, the enamel expression, by segments, dissolving. Winnie strode to the bed and snatched the picture frame from his hand. She glared at it fiercely, trying to locate what carnal attraction he had found in the photograph – a group of high school boys in their swim caps and trunks.

The swim team now sits on the dining room sideboard between Lucas's senior yearbook picture and a second-place swimming trophy. It won't stay there long, most likely. She'll move it to the nightstand in her bedroom until, for want of contented sleep, she commits it to her closet, to a padlocked chest, some airless place that Glover's thoughts can't reach.

She reappears in the bathroom door, a stack of *Awake!* magazines in her arm.

"I've asked Doris and Yolanda for lunch, Glover. I suspeck you'll be at the doctor's. In fact, don't bother with calling him. Just go there and give them my name. Alright? He'll take you. Just like before."

Glover feels the eye as it turns in its socket. There's a scraping sensation, as if it moves on sandy ball bearings. Winnie had clipped an orange bow to her hair and tarred some mascara to the ends of her lashes, which flap pointedly at the sink.

"Soap," she says.

The elevator shakes with the beat of the blaster. Heads bobbing, feet rocking, the boys, grooving in their Pepes and Phat Farms, seem not to notice Glover. On the ninth floor, they are joined by old Mr. Chu, with his plastic pail and fishing pole, on his route to East River Park. He winces at the music and shoots furtive scowls at their feet. The right side of Glover's head helplessly soaks up the bass. He finds it strangely invigorating. Like a transmission of amplified beehive activity. The boys disembark at the notorious fifth floor and a slender girl with armadillo curls and gold lipstick steps in. She looks dead flat at Glover's right eye. He withstands her gaze, watching the disgust compile in her face.

"Faggot," she says. "Pipsqueak cracker-ass motherfuckin' fag."

Mr. Chu in the corner coughs once, weakly. The girl veers for a moment his direction, then triple-snaps her chewing gum and swings her hips around.

The day is hot already. A gray haze stretches over the buildings of Campos Plaza Community Apartments and the soaring cliffs of Stuyvesant Town. Glover takes the courtyard to 14th Street, expecting to see Winnie and her old lady friends at the gate. But only Rufus White is there, his hands in his pockets, a green pick sticking out of his hair. Rufus – called Fufu by those half his age – wears clip-on neckties put on by his grandmother and likes to stand around with the Witnesses.

"Where they at, Dove?" says Rufus, unable to pronounce or remember "Glover."

Behind him, in the branches of a crab apple tree, Glover sees that the dirty gray webs of the tent caterpillars still haven't been cleared away.

"Check at the subway," says Glover. "If they're not there, they prob'ly went down to the Hall."

"Hall?" says Rufus, his brow bunching up.

"Kingdom Hall. By the Seaport. You been there a hundred times."

Rufus raises his head as if to nod, but freezes, peering down his nose at Glover.

"Where you goin', Dove?"

"Errands. See you later."

Glover hears Rufus's shuffle-step behind him.

"Dove! It hurts?" Rufus grabs him by the shoulder. "Your eye hurts?"

"Nah," says Glover, extricating himself. "It itches."

Rufus steps up, looks deep, draws back – just like Winnie had.

"It's red!" he says. "Red huuurts!"

"No it doesn't. Come on."

They stop at a T-shirt shop with a rack of sunglasses sitting outside. Glover claps on a pair with mirrored lenses in curvilinear, copper-colored frames.

"What you think?"

Rufus giggles, his head bobbling. "Phat, fine, flyyyy!"

Glover checks the sunglasses in the tiny mirror imbedded in the rack. Their breadth and curve hide the eye completely. He buys them with his lunch money, already feeling a certain relief.

Rufus turns when they reach First Avenue and makes for the subway entrance on the opposite side of the street. Winnie stands there with Yolanda and Doris, each holding Watchtower literature. When they see Rufus coming, they confer together briefly, then open to receive him.

Doris and Yolanda Banks are sisters. They're both in their sixties, share the same ostrich-like proportions, and dress like Munchkins. Doris wears a salmon-colored, ruffle-necked blouse and a knit skirt in green and black checks. Yolanda's ensemble is equally ecstatic, but with the added flourish of a pink corsage pinned to her jacket lapel.

Just when Glover thinks they've missed him, Doris waves his direction and shouts. Winnie whips around. The distance of the intervening crosswalk does not observe the connection between them – the IM's flash transmission. She gives him a cursory wave and smile, then turns her back to him. Rufus looks happy planted among them. He has already snatched up one of the magazines and is waving it over his head.

The traffic light changes. In the crosswalk, Glover passes an old man with a clear plastic shield fixed over one eye. The man walks unsteadily, glancing back and forth, as if the street is riddled with mobile sinkholes that could swallow him into the sewers. At a bus stop shelter near Second Avenue, Glover sees a lady with a similar shield. She looks at him pointedly, her lips parting as if to speak. Beneath her uncovered eye hangs a small yellow sack of skin. He quickens his pace, glad for the shield of his sunglasses.

The wail of sirens obliterates the lingering resonance induced from this encounter. Two squad cars and an EMS van zoom down 14th Street. Behind him, a fire truck rolls out of its station and makes the turn up First Avenue.

Now Glover remembers the Eye and Ear Infirmary, its banners hanging right over his head. Such an alien term, infirmary. Medieval. Like heated forceps and floppy-hatted nuns.

Glover walks by without looking in. Passing the optical store at the corner, he turns down Second Avenue.

Infirmary, nunnery, orphanage – modern medicine and social workers should have wiped such words from existence.

"Winifred Ramos," confirms the receptionist. She's a middle-aged Goth-chick dressed in black, with tattooed arcs for eyebrows. "And what is your name?"

"Glover Thomas."

"I'll see what we can do."

Glover takes a seat in the waiting room across from two others: a college-aged girl with her arm in a sling, and an elderly woman not a day short of ninety, her hair like a bubble of finely spun vinyl. Their pointed stares, deflected by his mirrored glasses, fall back to their habituated voids. The old woman looks at the metal cane standing beside her on its rubber-tipped toes. The girl looks at the coffee table. Its rectangular glass top is positioned so low that Glover can see her knees – and the underside edge of her pink skirt (and the dark void beyond it) – reflected in the glass. The girl is wearing black underwear or nothing. She adjusts the sling with her good hand, her knees edging carefully together.

There are more shifts of posture, barely noticeable, as if his fellow patients are both acclimatizing to the new dynamic that he has introduced. He pushes the sunglasses snug to his brow and stretches his legs as far as the table permits.

On his first visit to the clinic, Winnie had come with him. They had spent two hours in the waiting room – time that Winnie had managed to fill with an account of her religious beliefs. The only part that Glover remembers is that three types of people inhabit the universe: the *Anointed*, very few in number, who will help Jehovah rule His kingdom; then all the rest of the Watchtower faithful, called *Jonadabs* or the *Great Crowd*, who will be the citizens of that kingdom; and those that Jehovah will "rejeck" and destroy, including liars, adulterers, murderers, homosexuals, and those belonging to the synagogue of Satan.

Finally, the nurse had called his name.

"Tell Doctor Rivera what you saw." Like show and tell, Winnie took the framed photo from the plastic bag she had brought it in. "What did you see here to do that to?"

"Mrs. Ramos," Rivera protested. He was a tall, good-looking man in his forties. "Maybe it's best to leave us alone?"

"It's good for him," she snapped. "What is it, Glover? My son's legs? Is that it – his swimmer's legs?"

She seemed to have forgotten that Lucas was not the only boy pictured. But among the five other bare, wet chests, Lucas's was definitely finest. One arm was raised in a silly wave or salute, the line of the triceps crisply defined. His lips were puckered in good-natured confidence as he mouthed something to the camera. The photo cut off just below his thighs, the hairs on them combed by rivulets of water.

Just thinking about it, Glover feels a shift in his pants. As if to combat this rival sensation, a pointed itch takes hold of his eye. Closing it firmly, he turns it back and forth against the lid.

"Myrna Goldberg?"

A nurse stands in the doorway smiling. The elderly woman pries herself up, assisted from above by her Zeppelin hair. Glover lifts the sunglasses to get a better look. As the wispy dome floats down the corridor, an overhead light flashes harshly off the cane.

Glover drops the glasses back to his nose and braces himself for the added irritant. He keeps the eye still, holds his breath, tries to forget the prodding at his waist band.

"Tell the doctor what you were looking at." Winnie thrust the photograph in his face. "Answer me! What did you like about him?"

"When you fantasize, Glover," said Dr. Rivera, attempting a measure of professional autonomy, "do you only think about males?"

Glover slouched in his chair and stared sullenly at the floor. With a dike-bursting sigh, Winnie forged ahead.

"Answer me!"

The doctor retreated to the examination table, waiting for her to finish.

"His arms," Glover mumbled, just to say something.

"Okay," said Winnie, her left foot tapping at the floor. "His arms. What else?"

Glover glanced at the doctor. Rivera nodded encouragingly.

"His stomach," he said with a little more conviction.

"What about it?" said Winnie.

Glover looked at her then. It was like stepping across a treacherous bridge, the placement of each foot unsure.

"The way it ripples." His voice trembled as it rose. "The little hairs on it. And his chest."

"Dios mio." Winnie straightened. "What about his chest?"

For the first time, she appeared to be listening.

"The way it looks hard and soft at the same time." Glover could feel the air on his teeth. He could feel Rivera watching him. The bridge fell away.

"I like his hips and his legs and the way his crotch sits in his trunks, his dick pressed up with his balls."

Winnie's face went lax. She shoved the picture back in the bag and sat down. Glover felt the blood red-hot in his cheeks.

Rivera continued the consultation, his tone rigidly tender.

"Of course, I wouldn't encourage pursuit of such fantasies. It's easy to get into habits of thinking." He glanced at the polished steel of his stethoscope. "But, really, we know more about these things than we used to. Maybe some counseling would be good. For both of you, eh?"

He ventured a well-meaning look at Winnie, who rose from her chair like a very dense, extremely toxic cloud of smoke.

A mosquito shrills faintly in the waiting room. Glover hears it first near the window, then toward the elevator, the sour sharpness flavoring the air. He tries to ignore it, this plaint or directive from an alien world, from the hairy swamps of the Mesozoic.

"Would you pass me that magazine?" The girl nods at the coffee table.

"Which one?" he says, still trying not to move.

"The only one there. *Premiere!* Hello!"

He complies, though he has to sit forward to do it.

"Thanks," she snorts. As she thumbs noisily through the magazine, her knees, across the reflective table, slowly spread outwards.

Glover looks at her cradled arm. Even through his sunglasses, he can see the swollen fingers hanging off the end of the sling. They have a brownish-gray color and bruise-black nails. As if cognizant of his probing eye, she carefully shifts her wrist in the sling. The fingers pull at each other, a film of sweat, dirt and pain sticking them together. Glover's eye twitches. Their respective ailments, each on alert, send out countless microscopic tentacles to assess the other's defense capabilities. Her blackened nails are the only curb to the festering poisons readied for dispersal, just as the sunglasses, Glover decides, keep the safety on the pinkeye trigger.

As if to thwart any diplomatic efforts, the whine of the mosquito encroaches.

He feels a tingling in his left eye now. A leak must have sprung in the dam. He detects a seepage, an entire terrain being inundated. He thrusts up, scraping a shin on the coffee table, and hurries to the bathroom. He locks the door, removes his glasses, bends close to the mirror.

The left eye still shows clear. No redness yet, at least compared with its brother – the ascendant twin – whose territorial ambitions are garishly apparent. Glover turns on the spigot, his gaze locked to the arabesque of blood vessels etched around the iris.

On the way home from the first doctor's visit, he had told himself to prepare for a change. Winnie Ramos would lose no time in contacting the case worker. He had expected imminent expulsion. Days passed, then weeks. A reprieve had been granted, the length and conditions of which were never clarified. She cooked his meals and bought him clothes at the Old Navy sale. But she watched him, waiting for just the right moment – his most vulnerable – to drop the other shoe.

"Fuck you." His eyelids narrow as he speaks the magic words. The lower right lid is beginning to unravel; he can feel the single thread that composes it disengaging row by row. The lid has a purplish cast to it, like the girl's fingers in the sling.

This much he knows: the status initially granted him, though never explicit, had been irreversibly revoked. He had been "weighed in the balances," to quote Winnie's favorite Bible phrase, "and found wanting." He should have known it when she snapped her back to him at the subway – a careless giveaway on her part, a rejection reflex. How many other gestures had he missed, how many involuntary cringes and double-takes and furtive Lysol spritzes?

"Fuck you, Winifred."

He turns off the spigot. The hum of the mosquito pricks his ear. He can see it in the mirror, right over his head. It lowers steadily, drawn to the fruiting bog – the malaria, the typhus. He swipes at it, whirls around and swipes again. The insect retreats to a corner near the ceiling. He flings his sunglasses at it. They hit the wall and clatter into the sink, harmless and unharmed. Cheap shit. He stuffs them into his shirt pocket.

"Glover Thomas?"

The nurse is calling his name. His stomach tightens. He turns to the mirror. With his little finger, he cautiously dabs at the pus-filled corner of the right red eye. Then – a trepid smile, a cringe of valor – he brings it to the surface of the left eye. Just one little, lingering dab. Enough to ensure transmission. At once, he feels the germs taking root, the files, from folder to folder, transferred.

The girl looks up as he emerges from the bathroom. She catches her breath, unprepared for such an unveiled exposure. Her lips curl back. Her arm turns to salt.

"Glover Thomas?"

He tramps past the elevator to the stairwell door. The letters of the EXIT sign emit their lava light, a warning.

"Young man, the doctor is waiting."

He pushes out, taking the stairs by threes to the street.

The fervor of a righteous heart guides the storm of his passing. Each footfall shakes the veils of soot and carbon monoxide hanging in the air. The cracked sidewalk, the spindly ginkgo, two squatter types chaining bikes to a lamppost – each registers the passing threat, for he refuses to shield the infection with his sunglasses. An emaciated woman with two bags of groceries steps to the side, eyes averted.

Against the harsh Millennial light, his own gaze rages defiantly ahead. It confronts a fruit stand, frisking a ziggurat of Haitian mangos. It brushes the fur of a tethered pit bull and moves on, assaulting two oncoming pedestrians ignorant of the desecration done them. It lurches toward the back of an orange knit cap on the head of a black boy waiting at the crosswalk. As if sensing the danger, this boy, in his mid or late teens, turns his head slightly, then moves into the crosswalk. He wears a white tank top and saggy jeans of the type forbidden to Glover.

The color of the cap seems to vibrate around it, forming a series of electric halos. They incite the germs in the left eye to multiply. Winnie's sterilizing efforts that morning had been justified. The slightest touch was enough to establish a whole colony of invaders.

The black boy glances over his shoulder, his blue-mirrored sunglasses (genuine Oakleys, with gunmetal frames) flashing in the light. He turns back and keeps walking, but deliberately slows his gait. The sinuous lines of his triceps harden as he slips his hands in the pockets of his jeans. Glover, wishing only to pass him, quickens pace.

"'S'up, baby?" The voice emits a saccharine mist, sticky to the ear, cloying sweet.

Glover concentrates on his mission, launching red darts at promising surfaces – cell phones, shirt buttons, parking meter dials. He is placing the rungs of a living ladder, a bridge of sprouting petri dishes, that will carry his gospel to the whole Eastern seaboard. By nightfall it will board the last water taxi at the Christopher Street pier.

"So serious, baby. Why'n'cha come play?"

For a stubborn moment, the orange stocking cap and Oakley sunglasses hold parallel. Then they are swept into the roiling backwash, there to slosh and churn with the stagnant sea of plastic bags, clumps of hair, empty spray cans and the porridge of rotted newspapers.

Glover hears the boy's laughter behind him, like a lashing tail, with a hiss of both dismissal and challenge. It distracts him from his purpose, throws doubt on his previous work. Glover elects to glance behind him: he hears, yes, and he chooses to ignore. The black boy saunters playfully, his hands moving inside his jeans pockets; he grins, touching his upper lip with his tongue.

Glover whips around. He collides with a man just turning the corner. Packages flop on the sidewalk, boxes and cardboard envelopes tumbling, the colors of Federal Express.

"Jesus Christ! Watch where you're going!"

Glover, stooping, tries to help. The man pushes him off.

"Get the fuck away, little fuck!"

Glover takes a few steps, continuing on.

"You! Hey!"

Glover stops when he should just keep going. Mr. FedEx stands glaring at him, legs spread, packages every which way in his arms.

His posture changes – a shift of weight, a tilt of the head. He has seen it. Something about the eye sets him off. He drops the packages and springs forward, both feet leaving the ground at once. Glover bolts up the avenue.

"I'll fuck you up, you queer-ass little bitch faggot!"

After two blocks, Glover thinks he can still hear the man in pursuit. He is afraid to look back. Reaching 14th Street, he turns the corner, heading right toward the banners of the Eye and Ear Infirmary. He ducks in through the doors, his lungs ready to rip from his chest.

The waiting room has the feel of a bus depot, a veneer of seediness to it. No windows, high ceiling, a hollow square of vinyl-upholstered seating units in the center. On the wall to the right stands a long, high counter with two reception stations marked by yellowed computer terminals.

"May I help you, son?"

A fat white security guard with a shaved head and a wax-sculpted mustache approaches.

"My mother," says Glover, his eyes at half-mast; he should have put on his sunglasses before barging in. "I'm supposed to meet her." He tries to calm his panting. "She's having an operation."

"What's her name?"

"Winnie Ramos. Winifred."

"Take a seat. I'll see when she was scheduled."

Glover picks a spot with his back to the doors in a section where no one is sitting. Just a minute he needs, two minutes, enough time to clear the street of danger and to calm the knot in his stomach. He dons the sunglasses and looks around cautiously. Most everyone is old or retarded-looking, scattered in groups of twos and threes. The air of restless boredom around him overlays a more insidious and deeply rooted malaise. The word "infirmary" is entirely appropriate.

The run has spurred a frenzy in his eye. Like an anthill under Code Orange.

"What's the name?" He hears the guard at the door, and another voice answering: "Dupres. Cataracts."

His first day at Winnie's, she had walked with him to the East River Park, taking the foot bridge over the FDR. Everything was so derelict there, half the boardwalk fenced off. Unlike the other side of Manhattan (he had been to the Hudson River Park with the Liptaks), where the grounds were landscaped, everybody wore stylish clothes, and boys just a year or two older than he was hung out on the pier and rubbed sunscreen on each other and even kissed sometimes. But there he sat on a broken-slatted bench, watching anthills built in the rifted concrete while Winnie talked to Mr. Chu, who always fished from the same spot and never said a word to her. Glover had noticed that the level of activity among the anthills was consistent; when one got busy, they all did at once. Was it something in the ground, or the time of day, or a signal sent by microscopic transmitters? Maybe the anthills were connected through a network of tunnels in the pavement.

The three-block run to escape the FedEx man had decidedly stirred up his eye. Both eyes. The microbial traffic moves freely now through a passage significantly widened.

Glover gets up and makes his way through the lobby, his gaze fixed to the sign that says "lavatories." Tucking his glasses into his pocket, he enters. A man with a bandaged ear washes his hands at the sink. Glover posits himself at a urinal, waiting to have the mirror to himself. The man continues to wash his hands, sighing disgust every time the motion-triggered spigot cuts off. The hand dryer, too. When he finally leaves, someone else comes in and stands at the urinal beside him.

"'S'up, baby?"

Glover drills his gaze to the wall, imposing a kind of vertigo on himself, as if he stands at the edge of a cliff far removed. Yet, the red nets draw everything into their orbit – from the orange Kangol cap to the Nike Prestos. They sense the eyes behind the Oakleys turning. They register the movement of the muscled arm. Glover keeps his eyes to the shiny white tiles six inches in front of his nose. The mordant glare of antisepsis sets its blades against him. He can smell its challenge: submit or resist.

On the Internet at the Tompkins Park library, he had read that the human body harbored more than five hundred species of bacterial cells, more than eighty trillion in all. How many were seething in his eyes at that moment? How many surge through his veins and arteries? How many coat the tongue in his mouth or the tongue of the boy beside him? And if his bloodstream carries all these alien cells, how much of it can he call his own?

The older boy edges back from the urinal, exposing his own blade of challenge. He gives a squeeze to the end of it and tucks it under his sweatshirt.

"Come play, baby."

In the reflection of the tiles, Glover watches the orange cap recede and the door to the stall behind him open.

Each throb of his heart trips a response in the red web. With every contraction, his complaint roots further into the ocular membranes, taps into his matrix of blood pipes, inspiring a pointed resonance elsewhere, like a contained hemorrhage, which holds there, as in a knotted balloon, the stubborn, irresistible itch.

Glover glances toward the sink and the door. Someone could burst in any moment – the security guard with the weirdo mustache, the fuming FedEx man. There might be cameras here. He looks back at the tiles, at the dim reflection of the Kangol cap in the frame of shadow behind him. He takes a breath. The sides of the urinal touch his forearms – cold porcelain, germs. He puts on his sunglasses, takes another breath, then turns and slips quickly into the stall.

* * *

Yolanda Banks stands at her living room mirror. With her mouth whorled in concentration, she pins a corsage of satin rosebuds onto her jacket lapel. In such a pose, she looks every minute of her sixty-two years, but as she straightens her shoulders and lifts her chin, her age recedes to the odd swath of white that bursts through what is otherwise normally-graying, coarse, brown hair. She wears it in the style that she has for twenty years, bobbed sharply at the nape and with bangs to her eyebrows.

She checks her watch and grabs her bag. She must take a bus down to Kingdom Hall to renew her supply of pamphlets and magazines before meeting her sister and Winnie Ramos for their Tuesday Pioneering. She can hear them teasing her about the corsage: "So was your favorite Elder at the Hall this morning? We'd hate to see you get dolled up for nothing." To which she would answer in all good humor: "That's for me to know and you to pray about."

With a final frisk to the pink corsage, Yolanda steps into the corridor. Before she can turn to lock the door, she is met with the stare of her neighbor, Mrs. Brown, a stick of a woman with a bony head capped by a tight, curly, copper-colored wig.

"Get your trashy ass back to five!" she snaps, glaring straight at Yolanda. The wig is so tight that it puts the old woman's glasses off-kilter. "And don't come up to this floor no more, like your granddaddy still be livin'!"

Down the hall, a girl with gold lipstick and a frilly tank top sulks at the elevator. Even twenty feet off, Yolanda can sense the tension in this girl, in the volatile bounce of her hip.

"What has she done?"

Mrs. Brown renews her siege of Yolanda.

"I ain't her grannie, Miss Banks," she glowers. "Ain't nobody lef' here love that tin can hussy!"

The elevator bings and the doors edge back. Getting in, the girl launches a missile of obscenity down the corridor. In the light fixture overhead, a fluorescent tube flutters off and on.

With the girl's departure, Mrs. Brown has nothing more to impart. She stands there, uncertain, in her nightgown and slippers.

"I was sorry to hear about your husband," says Yolanda, careful not to break eye contact as she locks her apartment door. "I'm sure you must pass many lonesome hours."

The old woman nods, her glasses settling back on her nose. Mr. Brown had become disabled from a stroke and, after months of physical therapy, had ended up taking his own life (with a boning knife, according to Doris) while his wife was shopping at C-Town.

"You might find comfort at our Kingdom Hall. If you'd care to go with me sometime – "

Mrs. Brown stiffens, the engines of her eyes firing.

"No, Miss Banks, I believe in the Trinity, and you can tell old Satan that I told you so!"

It is a hot, humid morning, with only the barest tinge of blue to the sky. Thankful for even a mild breeze, Yolanda walks by the crab apple trees in the courtyard of Campos Plaza. She stops at one of them to examine the tent worm nests in one of the lower branches. The web-like nests appeared in June, at first white and dewy, then darkening with soot as the creatures they sheltered grew fat. It is the first day she has seen them outside of their nests. Four of them cluster on a branch near the trunk. They are soft and black, about an inch long, and are edged with fine gray hairs. One sits on the underside of a twig, its tender body clutched to the wood as its mouth assails a leaf. They must be preparing for their time of transformation. Any day now, they will forsake the communal nest completely to spin individual cocoons.

Malacasoma Americanum. She had written it down to remember it – the genus and specie of moth they will become. The larvae are known as tent caterpillars due to the structure of their pre-pupal homes spun out on the ends of branches. These facts – and so many others on so many subjects – Yolanda has gleaned from the Internet with the help of Glover Thomas. Given her persistently curious nature, she recognizes that such a pastime could seriously distract from prayer and Pioneering, but the interaction with Glover at the library was a kind of ministry in itself. Glover is a very alone type of kid. Not that she presumes a bond between them. Like most kids that age, he seeks the communion of his peers.

As *she* does with Elder Odibo.

Which is beyond (as she had explained to Doris) a prurient, physical or even intellectual, interest. Dennis Odibo, Yolanda knows in her heart, is one of the Anointed class. The power of Jehovah communes through his eyes. Each time he looks at her, it is like Moses parting the waters, allowing the Truth of the study lesson to approach her weak understanding. His odd and meticulous pronunciation lends a weight to his words that Elder Johnson can't match, or Elder Suarez.

When she told him about her neighbor's suicide, he replied in his Ghanaian accent: "So sad, what Jehovah's Truth could have made him, especially in the throes of his affliction."

It was Elder Odibo who taught her the goodness of Works and the privilege of being a slave to God, of being a Jonadab. He counted himself among the Jonadabs, too, and joyfully so: "Without the existence of the worker bee, the hive cannot continue."

But in the world to come, Yolanda knows, this man from Ghana will number among the One Hundred and Forty-Four Thousand specified in the book of Revelation. One night she had even dreamed that he was standing before Jehovah's Throne, his white robes enhancing the darkness of his skin, his uneven mound of silver hair burnished in the Judgment light. Then the radiance from the Throne had burned off his robe and he had danced naked on the Sea of Glass, his body swaying to the music of trumpets and pipe organs, much the same as King David must have danced before the Lord.

That the bus is overly air conditioned is something she should have prepared for. An old blind couple, both in sweaters, occupy the seats behind the driver. Yolanda has seen them in the neighborhood before, maneuvering the streets with their long white sticks. She sits across from them, next to a smartly suited young man on his cell phone.

Passing the library, she remembers the first time that she saw Glover there. He was fixed at a computer, so engrossed on the Internet that she had almost thought it selfish to intrude. But after the initial embarrassment (he quickly closed the web page he was studying), the boy seemed quite willing to engage her. He, too, had noticed the webs in the crab apples. Next thing she knew, he was showing her how to search for sites and images. Once they had matched the name and face of Malacasoma, they had Googled pictures of all kinds of caterpillars, some fleshy and hairless with bizarre markings, some like miniature porcupines.

The old blind couple sit holding hands, their faces utterly lax. They must have no inkling that their seeing counterparts make an effort to present an air of self-possession in public. Yolanda wonders how they met and how they preserved their own history together. Obviously not in photo albums. No snapshots to remind them, or confirm recollection, of significant points in their lives. What did a snapshot do anyway, but reduce an event to a single reference point, so that the snapshot itself became referred to in memory as representing and containing that event?

The old man cocks his head to the right, his oyster eyes turning her direction.

Usually the Hall is cleaned on Mondays, but, on entering, Yolanda hears the vacuum cleaner running in the sanctuary. Standing in the vestibule, she sees a large Bible with a navy blue cover laying on the bench by the coat rack. It is Elder Odibo's. She can tell by the ribbons sticking out of it, the brightly colored strips of silk he uses for bookmarks. If Sissy Crocket had another spell of asthma, Dennis might have been asked to vacuum today. As if he didn't have enough responsibilities, what with service leadership, nursing home visitations, and study lessons.

Yolanda finds herself drawn to his Bible, an object he treated with such a light-hearted kind of reverence, as someone else might treat a scrap book or diary. Bending down, she runs a finger over the cover. So many places he has marked, passages of special relevance for him. She has no right to intrude on these. She does, however, very gently, lift the cover. A bookplate marks the volume as his own: W. D. Odibo, Ph.D. He had never mentioned that he had a doctorate, but then secular honors were not particularly valued by the Watchtower. She might have been calling him Doctor all this time. His address is listed on the bookplate as 71 Bethune Street, along with a 646 phone number. An odd satisfaction percolates in her stomach, as if, until now, she has not quite believed that he existed in the flesh, in New York, in her life. He must have mentioned that he lived in Manhattan.

Leaving her bag in the vestibule, Yolanda enters the sanctuary. The burgundy carpet has already been vacuumed. He must be cleaning one of the study rooms. This pleasant coincidence is just what she hoped for, and the bus ride had precipitated a question that she wanted specifically to ask him.

"Questions, questions," he will chortle, his long dark fingers patting her hand. Yolanda imagines the glint in his eyes, the mixture of amusement and forbearance her quandaries always bring.

But how silly – the subject has flown right out of her mind. She stands outside the teen study room, hoping that the Hoover will continue its roar until she can remember it.

Oh, yes – the couple on the bus. For people who were blind from birth, she had wondered, what kind of dreams did they have? What kind of memories, with only the reference of sound and smell, touch and taste? Or did they necessarily invent images for things they had never seen? So in the book of John, when Jesus healed the blind man by rubbing mud on his eyes, both the man's waking time and his time asleep were changed forever. Had Jesus deemed it a richer life, or did the miracle have more to do with glorifying Jehovah?

Carefully, Yolanda leans in through the doorway. She would like not to startle him. But the surprise is hers, for it is Elder Johnson, not Dennis Odibo, who is doing the vacuuming. Bent over, the corpulent, white-haired senior Elder pulls a clot of something from the cleaner head. He glances up, red-faced and sweating. Yolanda nods to him and withdraws, hoping that her disappointment was not too flagrantly apparent.

In the vestibule, she takes twenty copies of the magazine – ten in English, ten in Spanish – from the rack of literature. She cannot help glancing at Dennis's Bible. He must be in the building somewhere or have stepped out for coffee or something in the neighborhood. The Hoover shuts off. She can hear Elder Johnson padding through the sanctuary. With Yolanda, he has retained a formal, falsely avuncular interface. He does not unfold easily, at least not to her.

"Hallo, Miss Banks." His recent visit to the London chapter of the Watchtower Society put a lingering stamp on his accent.

"Good morning."

"Terrible day to be running around. You'd be well advised to wear a hat, I should think."

"Elder Odibo is here?"

"He was indeed."

"He left his Bible."

Elder Johnson nods, a pointedly vague significance in the gesture. His gaze drops to Yolanda's corsage.

"Very flashy," he says, twitching his shoulders, as if to release accumulated sweat trapped in the folds of his body. By the way he says "flashy," it may or may not be a compliment.

Yolanda would never think of approaching him with her question. She knows that her restless intellect is her own particular weakness, ever having to humble itself before Jehovah's Truth. Elder Johnson's smugness would not accommodate her. The intellect, as he often proclaimed, is the "launch pad for pride and heresy."

"Is Elder Odibo coming back this morning?"

"I'm afraid not, Miss Banks."

He turns to the coat rack and begins to arrange the wooden hangers at consistent intervals. For such a large man, his hands are small and delicate.

"What's happened?"

He glances over his shoulder and meets her gaze with a squint.

"The Society, I regret to inform you, has dismembershipped Dennis Odibo."

Yolanda can only stare at him. Johnson responds with a bitter grin, as if to say that he has always suspected it would come to this.

"He has embraced the lies of the Pentecostals, the very infidels he was trying to convert. One must beware, Miss Banks, of the company one keeps."

Yolanda is so cocooned in her thoughts that she almost misses her bus stop. Only the chance sight of Doris and Winnie at the subway entrance plugs her back into the day.

"Good timing, Landa," says Doris. Her round face is dewed with sweat and her cheeks are a mottled rose color. "Down to our last magazine. What's wrong?"

Yolanda shakes her head and throws on a smile. She can't blurt it out right here.

"Your corsage," says Winnie. "It's crooked. Let me."

"It doesn't matter," Yolanda balks. "It's fine. Really."

Assuming her own Pioneering stance, Yolanda greets each passersby with a pleasant but not frivolous nod. Elder Johnson would not have lied to her. He would not have accused his associate falsely. The charge of apostasy, so extreme, would not be applied without a thorough confidence in the guilt of the accused. Had Dennis really abandoned his faith so utterly as to embrace Pentecostalism? He had always so pointedly criticized this particular sect of infidels: "To be *slain in the spirit* cannot mean also to surrender one's mind. We are told, are we not, to be sober and vigilant?"

Rufus White has suddenly joined them. Doris kisses him on the cheek, and Winnie, with more affection than usual, hugs him and pats his back. The young man fairly slobbers with pleasure. He snatches an *Awake!* from Yolanda's bag and thrusts it out with both hands: "Ge'cha *Post!* One cwaaaa-daaaaa!"

"No, Rufus!" says Doris, tapping his shoulder. "Our message is free, like God's love."

Without altering pitch or volume, Rufus calls out, "God has a name! God has a name! Je-hooooooo-vah!" He learned this from Elder Suarez's street corner witnessing. Yolanda, however, had read on the Internet that the spelling of "Jehovah" in English was not an accurate phonetic rendering. She had read, in fact, that God's name consisted only of vowels, most correctly represented in English phonetically as Y-A-H-W-E-H. Something she meant to ask Dennis Odibo.

"Glover won't be joining us for lunch," says Winnie. "He woke up this morning with a little problem and I sent him to Dr. Rivera."

"So that's where he was going in such a hurry," says Doris, fanning herself with a pamphlet.

Yolanda had been so distracted that she had not seen Glover at all. She asks Winnie if he is alright.

"Red huuuuurts!" Rufus wails. His eye has caught on Yolanda's corsage, where it lingers uncertainly before tearing away.

"It's nothing," says Winnie. "A little infection."

"Dr. Rivera is very competent," says Doris, adjusting her green and black checkered skirt, which has crept several inches to the right. "And such a nice, good-looking young man."

A fire truck careens onto First Avenue, sirens wailing. Two squad cars and an ambulance follow. To Yolanda, the noise is more piercing than usual, and recedes with greater reluctance.

"Dr. Rivera," says Winnie caustically, "does not think Glover's *tendencies* are sinful."

All expression drains from Doris's face, as if she's mentally shifting the pieces of a puzzle that she had previously misassembled. In about a minute, Yolanda thinks, her sister will restate her position.

"Now that you mention it" – less than a minute – "I do remember something strange in his manner when I had those plantar warts cut out. Something a bit too . . ."

"Winnie didn't say he was homosexual," says Yolanda. She will shoot that rumor dead in its tracks. This is how reputations get sullied. The same must have happened to her friend and councilor – a single remark misinterpreted, confirmed by coincidence, and reinforced beyond alibi's recall.

A man in a clown suit, a green wig and white face paint, stops in front of them. Yolanda greets him with a smile. He mimes his delight at having made her acquaintance, then pretends to set up a tripod and camera – one of those large box contraptions from the old days, for which the photographer had to cover his head and hold up the flash apparatus. Like in a Charlie Chaplin movie. They stand there stiffly as a group of pedestrians gathers, either to enjoy their humiliation or, even more perversely, to keep from passing between "camera" and "subject."

The mime, however, keeps delaying the "shot," attempting to compose them in just the right way. He first indicates that they should move closer together (which they do, inexplicably), then further apart. Rufus, oblivious to the ridicule, enjoys these antics thoroughly, even makes the faces dictated by the mime. Yolanda, caught between chagrin and amusement, can hardly keep from laughing.

At last, the "picture" is taken, the "flash bulb" is exploded, and the ecstatic performer, in fright wig and white-face takes the stairs down to the subway.

They return in silence to Campos Plaza. As for Doris and Winnie, by all appearances, the mime has managed to persecute them beyond any explanation. As if his make-believe camera had captured something shameful in themselves, which appeal to Jehovah's Truth did not entirely expunge. There was a ghost record, caught in his "flash," of perhaps a moment of defensiveness, of caring how the world perceived them. Even Rufus seems to suffer a pained introspection.

Yolanda is possessed of her own ordeal. Every subsequent minute brings greater anguish. As they enter the courtyard of the housing project, she feigns – God forgive her – an attack of intestinal flu. Which isn't exactly a boldfaced lie. A nervous wooziness bides in her stomach, growing in proportion to the certainty that she must speak to Elder Odibo.

"Flu?" Doris's glistening face mugs concern. "It was those deep-fry shrimps at the diner last night. I warned you, Landa."

"And the heat," says Winnie, avoiding embrace. "Feeds the germs. *Mi-ra.* Take a nice cool shower and get in bed. Can we bring you something?"

Yolanda declines, sweeping a hand through her white streak of hair. "I'll just step around to the Rite-Aid quick and get some Pepto."

So as not to stand guilty of another falsehood, she goes to the drugstore and makes the purchase. She asks the cashier if she happens to know the whereabouts of Bethune Street. The girl shrugs and, ignoring Yolanda's outstretched palm, plunks the change down on the counter.

Back in the heat, Yolanda hails a man in hardhat and goggles approaching her on the sidewalk.

"Excuse me, sir. Can you tell me if Bethune Street is in Manhattan?"

He meets her gaze through his plastic lenses and shakes his head as he passes her.

Yolanda asks a thirty-ish looking woman waiting at the bus stop.

"West Village," the woman answers, glancing at Yolanda's corsage. She looks familiar, with her dyed orange hair and lip piercings. "You can take any 14 bus." She nods down the block. "With this one, you'll have to get off at Eighth Avenue and walk down."

"Do I know you from Campos?" asks Yolanda.

"More or less." The woman thumbs a MetroCard from her wallet.

"I watch Rufus White sometimes when his grandmother goes for transfusions. She won't be doing that anymore, though. No use. Of course, you people don't believe in transfusions do you?"

On the half-empty bus, though the woman sits across from Yolanda, she immediately pulls out a book and starts reading. Her arm is tattooed with a hodgepodge of images: praying hands clutching a rosary; the words "*une rose est une rose*" in script underneath it; and, nearest the elbow and most proficiently rendered, the pyramid-eye from the dollar bill with its burst of light rays.

The Watchtower's stance on blood transfusions has always stumped Yolanda. It was the single point – as far as she knew – in which Dennis Odibo disagreed with his brethren. "The proscription in Leviticus is against eating blood, that is all, fresh blood." Quickly adding, "But if it indeed is fallacious doctrine, it is an error of human application, not of Scripture." By the tone of his voice, he expressed such views to nobody else.

Had she been wrong to trust so much in his judgment? How she had hoarded the advice he gave her, and the compliments. The first time she wore the rosebud corsage, he had said with admiration that the Queen of Sheba must have worn the very same.

She had become altogether too fixated on him, pulling up Internet sites on the post-colonial history of Ghana and the presence of Jehovah's Witnesses there. She had even Googled "Dennis Odibo" – something she'd felt a little guilty about – but found nothing but Odibo Hardware on Dennis Street in South Bend, Indiana. Of course, if she had known his initials at the time, she might have found something more.

Yolanda regrets that she didn't grab his Bible before she left the Hall. That Dennis Odibo had abandoned it was the most disturbing fact of the day. As if he had repudiated the faith entirely. Or maybe Elder Johnson insisted on it as a penalty of dismemberment, or was unwilling that it should be used in the service of heresy. The ribbon bookmarks Dennis used reminded her of Joseph's coat of many colors in the book of Genesis. When she told him that, he nodded: "It was a gift from his father, a sign of his love. So is the precious Word to me, a gift from my Heavenly Father."

"This is Eighth," said the woman across from her. "Walk south, about six blocks down. Bethune is just past Abington Square." She shoots Yolanda an oddly sympathetic, almost pitying, look. "Don't forget your bag."

A sudden breeze through the bog of heat registers at once on her fellow pedestrians. If it would only last: the easier breathing, the coolness on the brow, the clarity of thought and intention. A hopeful swath of unadulterated blue pushes into the sky from the west.

Yolanda hasn't been on this side of town since her mother's last days in St. Vincent's. The West Village, with its cobblestone streets, boutiques and posh eateries, is more generally a place for the young and well-heeled, like this Asian man with a feminine gait walking a dachshund and chatting on his cell phone. As Yolanda approaches, he looks right through her, until his gaze closes on her satin accessory. She hears him, too, as she passes him: "Oh, faggot, you should see what I'm seeing – Prom Night for Baby Jane," followed by a braying snicker.

The remark does not hit its target as intended. The corsage, for Yolanda, had quickly begun to lose the prestige with which she so vainly accorded it. And she is too preoccupied with thoughts of the coming confrontation to absorb such petty venom.

Confrontation is too strong a word. Clarification, explanation, "the scoop," as Doris would say. That's all. And if the worst were true, a resolution, a goodbye, a handshake, a hug.

Crossing Jane Street, Yolanda is surprised to see a dense little garden nestled between a lingerie shop and a liquor store. It is a glut of flora: phlox, daisies, hibiscus, hollyhocks, something that looks like a lilac but isn't, and a cherry tree, to judge by the bark. Here, such unchecked spontaneity seems like a breach of public order. And the branches of the cherry are blotched with webs – two drab, debris-speckled tents of that miscreant Malacasoma. She finds it strangely comforting to see this phenomenon on the West Side, too. The caterpillars are at the same stage exactly, dispersed here and there on the branches. A small hairy caravan troops up the side of a limb.

When Yolanda first saw them in Campos Plaza, they had incited mild revulsion. Revulsion and a wary interest. Then interest alone, a fascination even. Were these the first creatures to have infested Eden when Sin first entered there?

Eighth Avenue converges with Ninth at a triangular, landscaped traffic island. The orange-haired young woman was right. Just past this park, on the right side of the avenue, Bethune Street runs straight to the Hudson River, shining like brushed pewter in the distance. The breeze is holding. Yolanda feels the air at her temples, and the hair drying at the nape of her neck.

Here, already, is number 71. Yolanda halts and steps back several paces, as if her whole being is too far-sighted to take it in properly. The building must date from the eighteen hundreds. Its white-painted brick and worn embellishments – cast iron griffins flanking the steps –

could not be more charming or less ostentatious. The window boxes of the first floor apartments hold nothing fancier than red geraniums.

Yolanda climbs the four steps of the stoop and pushes open the door. The address on the bookplate might be out of date: only now does she think of this. Heart racing, she scans the panel of intercom buttons. Some are labeled with old plastic punch-letter strips, like the one she is looking for: Odibo, W. D. She presses the button, her stomach pitching as if down a well.

Dennis's Bible, if she had thought to bring it, would have provided an excuse for the visit, a lead-in. She wouldn't have to be standing in the foyer like a dog awaiting rebuke or embrace. It would have also given Dennis something to which he could easily attach his story. He would offer it willingly, nonetheless; she was sure of this. He was probably devastated, in dire need of a receptive ear, a kind word.

The hallway past the foyer door is lit with modern-looking sconces. The dark mouth of a stairwell waits at the end. Should she ring again? Now she hopes that he isn't home or won't answer. Silly. Again she presses the button.

There is a movement behind her. A middle-aged woman in a baggy T-shirt, jeans, and white hair cut similar to Yolanda's pushes in with four grocery bags. She sets the bags in a group on the floor and pulls a set of keys from her waist-pack.

Yolanda makes herself as small as possible. "Excuse me. Do you know a man here named Dennis Odibo?"

The woman fumbles through at least a dozen keys. "Nope." She has a flat face with the tiniest upturned radish of a nose.

"He's number 2C on the buzzers," says Yolanda. "Can I help with the bags?"

"The second floor buzzers don't work," says the woman, giving Yolanda a discriminating once-over. "Come in. He's expecting you?"

The woman doesn't wait for a nod or an answer, but unlocks the door, props it open with her heel, then, turning around and snatching up the bags, enters the hall, buttocks first.

"Sure I can't help you?"

"Nope. Thanks."

Ahead of Yolanda, and with four full bags, the woman mounts the carpeted, crooked stairs two by two. An odor permeates the second floor hall, a mélange of disinfectant, fat fryer grease and tangy cologne or aftershave, which Yolanda recognizes at once. As she knocks at the door of 2C, she remembers the comment of the man on the street in reference to her corsage. Does it make her look foolish? She had meant to take it off on the bus. She feels about for the pin securing it. A sharp prick to her thumb tells her where the point is located, but she can't seem to find the head. She drops her shoulder bag on the floor and fumbles about with both hands.

Footsteps approach the other side of the door. After the requisite peep-hole pause, a deadbolt snaps open. The door cracks to the length of the chain guard and a woman peers out through the interstice. "Yes?"

The surprise of finding a woman on premises, combined with the rip she has just put in her jacket, puts Yolanda in a state of paralysis.

Removing the chain guard, the woman opens the door far enough to reveal a young, heart-shaped, Hispanic face.

"What is it you want?" she asks, not unpleasantly. A gentle frown rumples the smoothness of her brow. "If you're canvassing for that City Council guy . . ."

"Oh, nothing like that!" Yolanda bursts out, a nervous giggle erupting. She grips the corsage with both hands.

"Then you must be Jehovah's Witness?" Again, with a gentle, sympathetic tone. She looks at the object in Yolanda's hands. "It's okay."

Yolanda has met this woman before. It was at Kingdom Hall more than six months ago. Her name is Carmina or something like it. She is Dominican and belonged to a Pentecostal church before attending a handful of study group meetings.

Carmina smiles. "It's okay if you are, ma'am. Jesus loves you just the same."

She had come to four or five meetings, two weeks at most. When she had stopped attending, people said she had reverted to her Pentecostal beliefs.

"Is that why you're here? To talk about the Watchtower?" She opens the door as if to demonstrate that she is neither annoyed nor defended. "Jesus can set you free of this slavery."

Yolanda tries to keep back the tears. She shakes her head. She cannot stay here. She thrusts out the satin corsage of rosebuds. "It's for him," she blurts. "He'll know it."

"What's the matter, ma'am? You're crying."

"Please!"

Carmina reluctantly takes the corsage. "Would you like to come in?"

Yolanda turns before the tears come hot. She reaches down to pick up her bag and makes for the dark of the stairwell. Carmina calls after her, but Yolanda, holding tight to the rail, takes the creaky steps down without pausing.

In the foyer, she stops, feeling faint and unsteady. She takes a tissue from her bag.

She had seen them together one night – Dennis Odibo and this

Dominican girl – at a restaurant on Avenue C. Until this moment, stepping into the sunlight, Yolanda has completely forgotten it. It was winter time. It was dark. They were sitting at Esperanto's, by the window, having dinner. Had it been the fact that they were sitting together or just how they were sitting that had caused her to pass two times by the window? They had certainly been conversing intently, Dennis leaning forward, his sharp African elbows on the table, Carmina with her head angled coquettishly away from him.

So many months later, Yolanda can evoke the smile on his face and the way he had patted the girl's wrist as he talked to her. Yolanda had passed by the window twice to mark the expression on each of their faces – even as fanged and feral jealousy hurled itself against the bars of her heart.

She had not intended to walk so far west, but here she is, standing at the West Side highway. The cluster of skyscrapers across the Hudson seems to have sprouted overnight. Since the terror attacks on the World Trade Center, Jersey City has grown by leaps and bounds. This skyline is completely new to Yolanda, as is the landscaped park across the highway and the white-framed towers in glass and steel rocketing up on her left.

Crossing the highway, she enters the park through a portal of shrubs and ornamental grasses. Flowers flock the curbs: lavender and black-eyed Susans and plants she cannot name. Small pines that she has never seen cast patches of shade on sculpted hillocks. Young locust trees line the boardwalk, where the benches and railings look freshly installed.

Beyond the rail, pilings sticking just out of the water trace the shapes of two vanished piers. These are the only remnants of the past. And herself. Yolanda Banks. The tears come again. Still, she does not feel old. Her sadness is not an anchor of despair or bitterness like her neighbor's, like Mrs. Brown's. It is a live thing, thrashing inside her like a spiny fish. It is the hurt of the young that Yolanda feels, a hurt that still has hope. There is pride – sinful pride – yet, in the flesh. She would not be without it on such a gorgeous afternoon, where the world has opened like a flower to the sun, and all things in it are new and lustrous, almost painfully so.

Crowds must flood this park on weekends. Even on a weekday there are joggers and skaters, tourists, the unemployed, seniors out for their daily stretch or drawn from their chairs by the promise of perfection – if they could only get closer to it. For the millionaires living in those stark condominiums facing the great wide West, what activity would not seem trivial in the face of such a vista?

A little further down the boardwalk a completely renovated pier boasts further plantings, a meander of grass, curvilinear benches. Small groups of young people sprawl about there. Mostly boys, it seems. But here are two girls – Japanese or Korean – in flowered little skirts and flip-flops coming toward her, tittering, and dipping their heads. One holds out a camera. "Photo?" she asks, indicating herself and her friend.

"Of course, dear."

Yolanda sets her bag at her feet and takes the expensive-looking instrument. She has never used a digital camera, and she points to what must be the shutter. Both girls nod eagerly, step back and pose, tilting their heads together and smiling. Yolanda motions them to the right, backgrounding them with a flower-ringed sculpture.

"Zoom!" says one of the girls, excitedly. She breaks the pose to point out the feature, then scuttles back to her friend.

Yolanda plants her feet for balance and, getting used to the viewfinder, zooms in and out. She composes the shot with the girls' faces in the lower left foreground, the sculpture in the center, and the edge of one of the pristine highrises toward the upper right. (She would take perfect pictures, Doris always said, if she didn't shake pressing the shutter.) Yolanda waits for a jogger to pass, then for two shirtless men holding hands. With her finger poised to shoot, she notices someone seated on a bench just to the right of the statue. He is not conspicuous enough to bother with except for the fact – and she zooms in to confirm – that it looks for all the world like Glover Thomas sitting there in a pair of new sunglasses.

After taking the shot, the girls step forward and thank her, nodding profusely as the Japanese do. She makes her way toward the boy on the bench.

"Glover? Is that you?"

His head snaps her direction. It is certainly Glover, and he is shocked to see her. He wipes a cheek with the side of his hand and looks back at the river.

She almost asks what he is doing here, but she veers off just in time. "A lovely day, isn't it?"

He grunts and shrugs his shoulders. He sits, slouched, with his arms folded and his knees spread wide. Like a street thug. He's been crying, she thinks.

"May I sit, Glover? Or do you want to be alone?"

Again the shrug, but she sits anyway, but not overbearingly close. He will share with her if he wants to. The sunglasses make him look cold and aloof, with their mirrored lenses and copper-colored frames. Still, she can picture the eyes behind them, light brown and gentle, acutely perceptive, chock full of secrets. Winnie is very strict with him. He is probably the only kid his age without a cell phone, certainly over here. Things like that are hard to bear for young people.

They sit together, watching a yellow water taxi approach the left side of the pier. Yolanda has never seen one before. The boat docks, allowing passengers off and on. Beyond it, a gigantic cruise ship, the Norwegian Dawn, glides southward, obstructing all but the tallest skyscrapers of the city across the Hudson.

NONFICTION

Deborah A. Lott

LOOKING FOR AN ANGLE

When I arrived at my Uncle Nathan's house that afternoon after a few days' absence, all signs of his dominion over the family room had been erased. The hospice nurses had opened the always closed shutters and taken away the bedside lamp by which my uncle liked to read. For the first time in months, maybe years, the TV sat silent. Instead, the sound of my uncle's breathing filled the room. With each inhalation came a raucous vibration that emanated from his throat or chest, or somewhere deeper, accompanied by a wet gurgle. I tried to tell myself that the sound wasn't particularly ominous, not so different from snoring – and hadn't Nate always been a king among snorers?

Nate remained in the middle of the room, in the hospital bed that had been positioned so he could still watch a baseball game on the big screen TV from bed. Even though he'd grown less and less capable of following the action, and no longer had money riding on the outcome, baseball held him in the realm of the living. "It doesn't take

Deborah A. Lott's essays have been published in *Salon, The Los Angeles Times, Lear's Magazine,* and *Psychology Today*. Lott's short childhood memoir, "Elephant Girl," appeared in *Open House: Graywolf Forum Five*. Her essay, "Trains," which appeared in *Alaska Quarterly Review,* was cited as a notable essay of the year in *The Best American Essays 2004*. This is her third appearance in *Alaska Quarterly Review*.

much to make me happy," he'd always said, "just give me a baseball game and a chili dog."

Set at a severe angle, the bed forced Nate into an unnatural sitting position. Though propped up by pillows on all sides, he slumped forward as though he might topple at any moment. As soon as I got close enough to see Nate's face, I realized he could not have been watching the TV even if it had been on. His eyes looked dull and vacant, his skin gray. I touched Nate's hand, but if my presence registered at all, it flickered faintly at the edge of a rapidly receding world.

Carrie, this afternoon's hospice nurse, moved to the foot of my uncle's bed and spoke to him in the syllable-elongated singsong of a nursery school teacher. She also dressed like one, her bulky, squarish body outfitted in scrubs in an oppressively cheerful pastel repeat pattern of baby animals and their mothers. "Can you hear me, Nate?" she said. My uncle nodded almost imperceptibly.

"You're doing just fine," Carrie said. "Just fine."

My Uncle Nate, my father's baby brother – my charming, voluble, eccentric, narcissistic, impossible Uncle Nate – was dying. He was the last blood relative of my parents' generation to succumb – the closest approximation to a father I'd had since mine suffered his final, fatal stroke when I was 29. The fact is, Nate had stepped in as a paternal figure long before that. When my maternal grandmother died from cancer when I was thirteen, my father let go of an already only intermittent grasp on reality. Whatever Nate's failings, he had one incontrovertible strength: when my father went crazy, he stayed sane.

Regarding himself as family patriarch, Nate dispensed advice for every situation. He bestowed nicknames on the boys I dated. "That Shlepperman's family is in the furniture business – that's good, people are always going to need furniture," or "Moronsky's got a funny chin – are you sure he's not mentally defective?" "Don't sell yourself short," he'd say. "So what if you grew up in a nutty family, you're still the prize."

Nate was bedrock and Nate was dying.

"It must be very hard to breathe," Carrie enunciated loudly from the foot of the bed, lifting her eyebrows and opening her eyes wide in a demonstration of empathy. Nate weakly mouthed "Yes," but lacked enough breath to make a sound. It took all his energy to hang on to this small measure of what he recognized to be life-and-death interaction.

"Would you like me to suction your airway?" Carrie held up a large plastic device with an intrusive looking curved end attached to a vacuum bottle.

My uncle shook his head with a little more vigor, "No."

"This is the only way I can help you breathe. Wouldn't you like to breathe better?"

An emphatically mouthed "Yes."

"Can I suction you then?"

"No."

This went on for several more rounds. As usual, my uncle wanted what he wanted but refused to accept the ordinary channels for attaining it. An inveterate gambler, he was always looking for an angle.

In the days since hospice had deemed Nate to be "actively dying," they'd begun to provide round-the-clock nursing. Continuity of care being a hospice value, I expected that Vladimir, the buff, kindly Russian male nurse who'd been treating Nate all along would be with him at the end. But Vladimir left on vacation, and a parade of unfamiliar contract nurses – Carrie the latest among them – arrived in continuous shifts.

Leaning over my uncle's side, Carrie examined Nate's forehead, then chest, then arms, in a state of gathering agitation.

"I knew it!" she said. "He's got scabies. Hasn't anyone told you?"

How could it matter now, I thought. Carrie yanked me by the arm across the room, and once under a bright light, thrust her own forearm before my eyes.

"Look," she said, tracing her finger over an indistinct rash of raised bumps and scars. "Scabies. I caught it from a patient."

I shrugged.

"For months no doctor could diagnose it. You only see what you're looking for. Otherwise you can miss what's right in front of you."

Carrie ushered me back across the room to my uncle's bedside where, after putting on fresh surgical gloves theatrically, she proceeded to pull down the sheet damp with Nate's sweat. Then she wrenched up his hospital gown, undid the velcro closures on either side of his adult diaper, and exposed his groin. His legs looked inordinately pale and thin, his pubic hair still blonde. Though he was the fairest person in my family, the blondeness of that hair still shocked me. Carrie spread the hair with her gloved hand and traced a path, connecting one red mark to the next.

"Scabies travel," she said. "See, you can follow their tracks."

What I saw didn't look any different from the mysterious eczema that had plagued my uncle ever since he returned from ground combat in World War II.

"I don't think my uncle would like this, I said. "His niece looking at his pubic hair." I knew I didn't like it and turned away.

"He should be quarantined immediately," Carrie said.

When I looked back at Nate, he silently mouthed the word "water." Like his brother, my father, Nate had always imbibed copious amounts of fluids – water, coffee, lemonade, soda, whatever he could get – and eaten massive amounts of food. As long as I could remember, if I called and asked Nate how he was, he'd respond, "Can't complain, I'm sitting up and taking nourishment." Consumption equalled health. But for days now, Nate hadn't been able to eat at all. He had reported this alarming loss to me, as he had each preceding decline, in an early a.m. phone call. "It's the daily medical report," he'd announce officially, before launching into a phonetic rendition of his latest lab result or the insert on his pain prescription. Born into a family of hypochondriacs, I'd taken the counterphobic tact of immersing myself in the facts of disease and becoming a medical writer. My family often called upon me to act as the interpreter. With Nate, I felt more strongly than ever the tug of an unspoken demand: if I could understand the words why couldn't I mitigate their meaning? While my family gave free rein to the hysteria that seemed our most instinctual response to any medical crisis, I had identified myself as the one who would remain rational.

But Nate's morning calls unnerved me. Before I'd had a chance to collect myself from sleep, before I'd even had a cup of coffee or spoken to my husband, Nate's still-booming voice would hijack me into consciousness: "I'm dying, goddammit," he'd say. As if I could forget. "Maybe if you took a little more Vicodin in the evening, you'd sleep better," I'd say. Or, "Ask for a bronchodilator to reduce the tightness in your chest." Focusing on the body to avoid the emotions. Nate had enough of the latter for both of us. His impending death not only saddened, but outraged him, it constituted the ultimate affront to his narcissism. If he'd survived WW II by contracting pneumonia and winding up in the infirmary on the day his company perished, how could old age have the audacity to get him now?

"I never really believed that anything bad could happen to me," he said. He'd had the same trouble at poker. He never believed a losing streak could last. Even with all the aces laid out on the table, Nate expected there to be one left in the pack just for him.

I couldn't believe it either and Nate knew it.

"Ah, you think I'm going to live forever!" Nate snarled on the phone one afternoon. "Otherwise you'd come and see me more often." "I'm on deadline," I said. "Forgive me for getting distracted by my own life." For the past few years, I'd held my work up as a shield to avoid marathon telephone conversations with Nate that had grown more and more one-way. He couldn't hear me over the phone and wasn't interested in listening anyway. He had so many life lessons to impart about his hero Winston Churchill, and the loss of civility, and how we "women's libbers" didn't understand men. Over and over again the same lessons: did I realize how much of a travesty it was that my grandmother never let me meet my grandfather? Not that my grandfather who was on the other coast ever tried to meet me, of course, and not that he hadn't died when I was still a very young child, but Nate still idolized his father and considered his mother the force that had kept him away. "He was a great, great guy," Nate said, "not a by-the-book kind of guy, not like your Socialist in-love-with-their-own-martyrdom parents. Maybe he could have convinced you that you shouldn't work so hard; only suckers work so hard when you can just hire other people and make it off their labors." No matter the contentiousness of the preceding conversation, my uncle always closed tenderly and with the same words, "Be a good girl." Who would tell me to be a good girl now?

Carrie brought a glass of water and raised the straw to my uncle's lips, but he didn't have enough breath to suck. Over and over he asked for water, and when the straw met his lips, could not drink. His repetitive, automatic asking reminded me of a battery operated toy whose wheels keep spinning even after it has crashed into a wall. Perhaps he could not remember from moment to moment that he could no longer swallow, or some satisfaction remained in the illusion of having his needs met.

Carrie's shift ended.

"Wear gloves," she cautioned Maureen, the incoming night nurse as they crossed paths at the front door. "Don't let it spread."

Maureen rolled her eyes. In her mid-50s, her rugged, deeply lined face suggested she'd spent a lot of time in vigorous outdoor activities. She'd pulled her graying blonde hair back in a severe ponytail, and wore simple rimless glasses. Maureen approached my uncle's bedside, stood silently, head cocked, listening to him breathe. The sound had grown louder and more insistent.

"Wow, it might be tonight," she said. "He might not even make it to morning." Maureen sounded excited, as if death were an event worthy of her attendance as opposed to the day-to-day monotony of caring for the terminally ill.

"What's that noise he's making?" I asked.

"Oh, that's the death rattle, honey," she said. "Didn't you know?"

My stomach lurched; although I knew that Nate was nearing the end, I did not want him to die today.

My uncle was at home with hospice largely at my urging. In the final months of my mother's life, though I comprehended that her congestive heart failure would be fatal, I was so terrified at the prospect of losing her that I instructed her doctors to do everything short of putting her on a ventilator to save her. I put her through indignity after indignity, torture after torture to keep some faded facsimile of her in the world. Her doctors colluded in these last-ditch efforts to preserve life at any price. They cheered each time an infection reversed, regarded it as a triumph whenever she emerged from delirium into a few moments of coherence. They seemed nearly as phobic as I was about her dying. Notwithstanding these efforts, of course, my mother did die – still receiving hourly breathing treatments, a feeding tube down her nose into her stomach, an IV in her arm. I didn't want to make the same mistakes with Nate and he took immediately to the notion of hospice; if the doctors couldn't cure his lung cancer, why should he let them "mess with" him? Besides, hospice provided better service, "I won't have to go to them, they'll all come to me!"

Hospice promised more than a way of avoiding unnecessary medical treatment. I anticipated a crew of gentle, selfless Mother Teresas, enlightened, otherworldly beings operating on some elevated spiritual plane. They would have learned how to accept death with grace and equanimity and could show us lesser mortals how to do likewise. Secretly I wished that they knew something, had seen something that could counter my visceral conviction that death meant a mere dropping off into the void. Perhaps, I thought, their faith would rub off on Nate as well. For my uncle and I shared a deep faithlessness and the existential angst that accompanies it.

When Nate first discovered Ernest Becker's book *The Denial of Death,* he called me. "This guy's got it exactly right," Nate said. "Everything people do is a way of denying they're going to die. We think if we make great art, or write a book, or *shtup* better than the next guy we're going to live forever. When I'm on a winning streak at the poker table, I feel immortal. But we're all kidding ourselves because we're scared. "Am I right? Don't you think I'm right?" On a roll, Nate demanded my agreement.

"I do," I said. "But people don't want to hear it."

My uncle and I both regarded death as annihilation, and annihilation as horrible.

Maureen took Nate's vital signs. I held his other hand, bluish along the nail beds. He didn't react.

"How do you do this work?" I asked.

Maureen said she'd been in the hospice business since the 1970s. She'd raised three children on it. "This work is all I do," she said. She didn't date, didn't have hobbies, she lived – Death. "This week, I've already witnessed three – if it happens tonight, this will be four –" she said.

So this is the Angel of Death, I thought, the one they send in at the end to seal the deal. The Closer.

However intellectually satisfying my uncle found the premise put forth in *The Denial of Death*, it brought him no solace when he was dying. As death impended, Nate grew panicky. He didn't long for an afterlife so much as another go-round at this one. "I squandered my life," he said. "I fucked it all up." He'd botched his marriage, wasted his talents, done too little for his sons. He demanded that hospice send him one "spiritual adviser" after another. Each in turn trotted up his doorstep, stood at the front door shouting until they could be heard over the blare of his beloved *The Golden Girls* and my uncle yelled for them to come in: Catholic priest, Protestant minister, and then, the rabbis.

"This rabbi they sent me is just a kid," he hollered into the phone one day, rejecting a pert but tentative young woman who'd shown up on his doorstep. "I need an old man like me, someone who's also facing death." I suspected he longed for the Orthodox rebbes he'd rejected during his Detroit youth, with their massive white beards and long black coats. But most of them were already gone. My uncle had renounced Judaism as a young boy, blaming his mother's Orthodox faith and her meddling religious parents for turning her against Nate's father, a gambler and roustabout. When their parents divorced when Nate was only four, my father allied himself with his mother's family and became religious; Nate with the maverick father whom he romanticized but rarely saw.

When a series of rabbis and none of the other spiritual advisers sufficed, hospice brought in a psychologist, social worker, and finally a psychiatrist. I'm sure Nate didn't bother to tell them that he'd already spent twelve enthusiastic years in thrice-weekly therapy, ranting and raving, before dismissing his therapist as a quack.

"We didn't have any rapport," he hollered into the phone about each of the advisers in turn. "I need rapport." In Nate's final days, hospice found him a mystically oriented psychiatrist who assigned the nearly 300-page *Tibetan Book of the Dead* for him to read. He could barely hold it up. "I can't get into it," he told me. "Not much of a plot."

Maureen and I stood at the foot of my uncle's bed as she appraised the situation.

"I'd wager he's about 6 centimeters dilated," she said. "Dying's like labor, there's no turning back. He's got to stop fighting it." She said it like a school teacher castigating a negligent student for not buckling down and doing his homework. "A woman with four young children I cared for," she went on, "metastatic stomach cancer – every time she ate, she threw up, but she wouldn't get the message and stop trying to eat. She didn't want to leave her kids, so she kept fighting it." Maureen shook her head, as if the woman were frigid and not allowing herself to have an orgasm. "It took her twelve days to die."

My mother's doctors had regarded death as an enemy combatant, the opposite of all things good in the Universe. Clearly their interventions seemed overkill on the side of life but now it started to seem as if Maureen had made her bargain with the Other Side.

"So what's the rush?" I asked.

"Death is just a physical process the body goes through," Maureen said. "There's no point in prolonging it. When people have one foot in this world and one foot in the other, they need a little help getting to the Other Side. I'm the midwife."

Having discounted other spiritual beliefs and practices, I'd held hospice in a separate category, the last sacred cow, privileged somehow by its proximity to death. If hospice workers hadn't glimpsed proof of an afterlife, evidence of some higher, ultimately benign meaning to human existence, then all felt lost. But talking to Carrie, and now Maureen, I began to think that as skeptical as I was, I'd still been naive: these women were just plain kooks, no different than the other New Agers who crowded the supplements aisle at Whole Foods perennially looking for the next miracle elixir, or the aura readers on the Venice Beach boardwalk. And then it occurred to me that if we still believed in Freud, we would not give hospice workers the status of saints. We would suspect unconscious motives in those who dedicate their lives to helping people die; we would expect them to derive some unconscious gratifications. A woman like Maureen who had no other life than helping people die just might hold some libidinal investment in death. She might get a charge from it, a little goose of erotic thrill. Balancing on the cusp of life and death, having her hand on the motor, being tuned into every downward turn, excited Maureen. Death enlivened her. She liked it. Or did I just need a target? Someone upon whom to project my anger at my uncle's death – anger being easier than grief.

"And what if there is no Other Side?" I said. Would it feel different for you if you knew there was no Other Side?"

"If I didn't believe they were going somewhere better, if I didn't believe we were all eventually going someplace better, I couldn't do this job without going crazy, now could I?" Maureen hooted.

"Have you ever seen any signs, any proof?" I asked.

"I've seen what I've seen and drawn my own conclusions. But we're not going to know for sure until we die ourselves, are we?" Maureen laughed.

Nathan groaned and Maureen delivered an eyedropper of morphine under his tongue.

"I wish he would go to sleep and sleep through this part," she said. "It's harder when you're awake." Was she suggesting he could sleep through his dying and never wake up? Or wake up for the good part at the end? *The good part?* If my uncle slept, what would he dream of – his own impending suffocation? I realized then that no matter how much he was suffering, I wanted Nate to hold onto every last minute of consciousness possible so that I could hold onto every last minute of Nathan possible.

"What do you suppose he's aware of?"

"How hard it is to breathe. I don't think it feels good. He probably feels anxious."

Please not that, I thought. On my father's side of the family, anxiety was the family curse. Nate had always dispelled his with three movies a day, multi-volume accounts of Hitler's last days, with gambling, venting, overeating, Irish whiskey, and women – or at least the fantasy of women.

A few months before his diagnosis, Nate drove me in his ancient Volvo over to the deli where he ate lunch every day. As we waited in line for the cashier, he nudged my arm, "This gal's got a thing for me," he said, loud enough for her to hear. He bobbed his head, trying to catch her eye. The cashier, a voluptuous Latina in her late 30s, appeared weary. She cast Nate the benevolent smile the young and beautiful bestow on the old and infirm. He nudged me again. I strained to regard my uncle as the cashier saw him – not as I usually perceived him, a composite of all the ages at which I'd known him, thirty-five and vital, playing baseball with his boys, a lawyer in a dark blue suit and flashy tie in his 50s – but only as an eighty-year-old. An unshaven, disheveled eighty-year-old with a shock of pure white hair standing straight up, soup drips down the front of his shirt, and an old man's dribble stains down the front of his pants.

"She's a lot younger than you are," I said.

"Ah, only American women care about that. Latin women revere their elders; they want a guy with experience."

"Can't you do something about the anxiety?" I asked Maureen.

She flipped through Nathan's chart. "The doctor should have ordered a tranquilizer," she said. "The morphine cuts the pain, but not the fear."

The thought of Nate, locked in one spot, trapped in the body and too weak to voice his anxiety even as it overtook him, seemed the ultimate punishment. Waves of queasiness spread through me; I felt dizzy and faint, trapped in my own body, trapped in my own hyperreactive nervous system. I didn't want to be here; I couldn't watch any more of this. I wanted to yell at every friend who told me that being with my uncle when he died would be awesome or inspiring. I wanted to run. If only I could just slip out of a side door, get in my car, and drive. That's what my uncle himself would have done – he'd avoided other people's hospital rooms like the plague.

For weeks my uncle had been asking for his misplaced gun.

"If I had my gun, I could take care of this myself."

"I'll be there at the end and make sure you don't suffer," I promised.

I couldn't leave. I picked up the phone.

"You'd better get over here now," I told my brother Paul. "It's moving more quickly than expected."

Half an hour later, Paul arrived. As I believe in nothing, my longhaired, intense, sensitive, eccentric, older brother Paul believes in everything – guardian angels, psychic messengers, visitations from other planets, life after death, ghosts among us. Always ghosts among us. Paul shut off his bedroom in the home where we grew up, and where he continued to live with my mother until she died, insisting that it was haunted.

"What went on in our own family was enough to haunt it," I'd say. But Paul insisted that real ghosts roamed the room, friendly but capable of turning on him. I woke up one night when I was twelve and Paul was seventeen to find him holding a chair over his head, trying to ward those ghosts off.

We shared a love of Nate. When Paul was a boy and at war with our father, he used to tell everyone that Nate, whom he resembled, was his real dad. "You know Mom was crazy about Nate," he'd say. "It only had to happen once."

Paul stood at the foot of Nate's bed and looked at him, shaking his head.

"Poor Uncle Nate," he finally said. "He was always my champion."

Eyes teary but blazing, Paul bounded over to where Maureen and I stood. "There's a lot of energy in the room, a lot of energy," he said. "Can you feel it?" Maureen smiled, urging him on. "You know, I lost my faith when my mother died," Paul said, "because no matter how much I missed her, she never came to me. I've been struggling to get my faith back ever since." Maureen nodded. "There really is lots of proof for an afterlife," Paul said, "even though my skeptical sister dismisses it." Paul and I reverted to the patterns of our childhood, triangulating whenever a parental figure came onto the scene.

"When they weigh the body after death it's always exactly twenty-four grams lighter, the weight of the soul that's exited, and what about John Edward's communiques with the dead relatives of the people on his show, there's no logical way he could know that stuff, and the white light seen by those who survive near-death experiences, and angels picking up people who fall down mountainsides and are unconscious and then wake up mysteriously transported to safer ground."

To me Paul's rant seemed a rapid-fire defense against acknowledging what seemed so obvious: to die was to be disappeared, absented, lost, annihilated. My uncle was already more than half-gone.

"Okay," I said, "so if people have souls that go somewhere when they die, then what about apes, and chimpanzees, our nearest relatives – at what point in evolution does the soul kick in? And what about dogs, and if dogs, what about hamsters, and worms and plants, and bacteria, how far down does it go? Why should we be singled out from all other forms of life?"

Paul and I had sparred on this subject so many times before it felt reflexive. He put his arm on my shoulder, as if he wanted to comfort me, and sneaked a conspiratorial glance with Maureen, "My poor little sister, she's always been so literal."

"Where's the economy in immortality?" I said. "An afterlife just seems so . . . inefficient. "I don't get it," I said. "I just don't get it."

"Why are you so resistant to spirituality?" Paul said. "You go through so much pain by not permitting yourself to be more open." He patted my shoulder and I pulled away.

What *was* so bad about feeling better that I had to reject it at all costs? Didn't a little self-delusion make life more tolerable? I'd held my rationality up as a defense, as if it could protect me from going crazy like my father, as if his craziness had resulted from a surfeit of belief. But faith didn't drive my father nuts; the Jewish faith of his boyhood had completely eroded by the time his mother died. Grief was what had driven him crazy; maybe losing the people you loved without any faith to sustain you was what made you crazy. And yet, once my father had lost his hold on rationality, the floodgates of belief opened so wide there was no limit to the bizarreness of what they admitted. And hadn't my brother Paul's capacity for faith become an indiscriminate appetite that could not be sated? If I willed myself to blind faith without requiring any empirical evidence, how could I be selective about what I chose to believe? How could I keep out the bad ghosts? And wasn't it my natural propensity to believe most strongly in the bad ghosts? Aside from that, should the mere wish for solace, the mere wish for something to be true, constitute grounds for believing that it was true? Wasn't our highest obligation as human beings, the obligation to seek truth? I owed it to my uncle to observe his death without illusion. If something should reveal itself, I would try to remain open to experiencing it.

Paul walked back across the room to my uncle's bed and put out his arms as if feeling for rain. Then he spun around like Julie Andrews in the opening of *The Sound of Music*. "Can't you feel the angels in the room?" he said, exultantly. "Oh, yes," Maureen said. "They're here." Maureen and Paul stared intently into one another's eyes. Was my brother flirting with my uncle's deathbed nurse? I felt left out. I walked across the room and stood right next to Paul so the energy could not escape me. I shut my eyes, spun around exactly as he had, once, twice, and then another revolution, and another, until vertigo forced me to stop. "I feel . . . nothing," I said, then started to cry. My uncle's face had grown twisted and contorted, every muscle and vein popping out with the effort to breathe. And that rattling sound made me want to scream.

"Just look at him," I said. "How can you not see what I see?"

"You always get stuck on the body," Paul said. "What you see is only the body struggling; it's no longer *him*."

"Is that supposed to comfort me?" I said. "When all I want is him. If he's not here anymore, where, exactly, did he go?"

Like a petulant child, I wanted my Uncle Nathan back, in all his unbearable one-of-a-kind self. Restored to his pre-disease state. Better than that, I wanted him back young again. Vital. The way he looked in his Army uniform at age 19, or clowning in the backyard with his mother. Able to start over and not fuck up his life this time. Further, I wished to start over again with him. I pictured us going back together and being the same age, rather than his being my uncle. If I could just get us out of our rigid placement in time, the permutations were endless: what if I were the aunt and he were my nephew; what if I were the mother and he were my child; I imagined all the ways of erasing, reversing, revising this moment. Anything but this inexorable now.

"It's changing now, can you hear it?" Maureen said. She had perfect pitch for the sounds of dying. I stood at some distance from my uncle's bed, watching him but not close enough to catch it, as if death were a contagious disease. My brother Paul, in contrast, danced his hands all over Nate, stroking him, rubbing him, willing comfort into him.

"Labor's picking up now," Maureen said. The metaphor seemed apt, Nate working hard to keep the oxygen coming in despite what Maureen called the "extreme congestion" in his chest. Weirdly isolated, Nate's abdominal muscles caved in and out violently below his ribs, in a fashion that no one, except perhaps a Yogi, could consciously produce. My brother stood over my uncle, held his hand over his head, and blessed him. "*Eev-a rechacha adonai Eloheinu,* May the Lord bless you and keep you. May the Lord cause his countenance to shine upon you and bring you peace." It was the Jewish blessing that Nate had last received at his wedding, and before that, at his bar mitzvah.

"It's okay to let go of the body, Uncle Nate," Paul said.

"No," I protested silently. But Nate had nothing in his hand left to play.

"I'd like to change his diaper; can you guys help me?" Maureen asked. My brother and I got on either side of the hospital bed and turned Nate onto one side. Paul held his back and I held his atrophied shoulder. As wasted as he was, he was still heavy. Then, with my hand on Nate, I remembered the way my uncle used to greet me as a child, *Debela,* he'd say, and pull me toward him with his powerful arms, and go for my head, pulling at my hair or rubbing the back of my neck, sometimes even slapping the top of my head to get my full attention.

"Ow, that hurts," I'd say.

"Ah, it does not," he'd answer. "Don't be such a fragile flower."

Combining self-protection and affection, I took to butting him with my head before he could touch me, pushing my head as hard as I could into his stomach and chest. I could never budge him. "*Debela,*" he'd say. "My little billy goat."

"I took a crap in the diaper for the first time," Nate had told me about a week before. "I didn't have the strength to get to the commode and the nurse said, "It's all right, just let go. So I did." It didn't seem to have bothered him much. In fact, Nate seemed to have almost enjoyed it, as if in that moment he reclaimed the ideal infancy he'd never had – doted on and worshipped by two united parents. It only took getting to 80 and being on his deathbed to achieve it.

Maureen spoke his name loudly, then pinched his arm just to check. "I don't think he's anxious anymore," she said and laughed. His mouth opened in a wide O with his lips pulled back over his teeth in a grimace that looked monstrous to me, unearthly. Then I realized that the gargoyles on buildings, the ghouls and monsters in horror movies were based on how people looked dying. We'd lost the connection because we just didn't see people die that often.

"Hold his hand," Maureen suggested. "Just because he can't react with his earthly body doesn't mean he doesn't know." I touched his hand – it shook hard, clenched the sheets with every remaining ounce of energy. Burning hot, the heat in his hand made me recoil.

"You get a fever when you die," Maureen said. "Too late for Tylenol now."

Maureen pulled the sheet back and pinched my uncle's white and nearly hairless legs. All the men on my father's side of the family had shapely, elegant legs. Gorgeous feminine legs. I tried to take every detail in, knowing that this would be the last time I would look at them.

"Look," she said, pointing at the purplish mottling.

The blood, unable to circulate, pooled in his legs, causing splotches of color.

"He's already dead down here."

Maureen delivered another dropper of morphine under his tongue.

The sights and sounds of my uncle's struggling intensified. If I couldn't bear to stay in the room with them, I felt too agitated to stay away. So I paced, around the bed, and then into the kitchen, and out to the laundry room, and back across the family room, skirting the bed, averting my eyes, and into the living room. I sat down on the living room couch for a few minutes and cried, but I could not stay still for long. Meanwhile my brother, his hand on Nathan's forehead, chanted and recited prayers, a melange of English, Hebrew, Buddhist, Hindi prayers. Again he delivered the generic Jewish blessing.

When I finally approached the bed, Nate's mouth had opened into an even more grotesque grimace and his arms shook as hard as if he were back in the butcher shop's walk-in freezer where he had worked as a young man.

"Why does it have to be so violent?" I said.

"Let's put on some music," Paul said. We went through the channels on the radio – country western – no, not his taste – 60s and 70s rock – too jarring – and found classical music. Chamber music heavy on the strings – the music to die by. We turned on the music on the pretense of calming my uncle but it was really to drown out the ever-more cacophonous death rattle.

"You know even if he were still capable of hearing the music, he was too deaf to hear it at this volume," I said, denying even the possibility of comfort.

"You never know," Maureen said, "he might be hearing it with other ears now." So, according to Maureen, my uncle not only had a soul, his soul had its own body. The duality made me dizzy. Why did other people's faith enrage me?

Back at the bedside, I took my uncle's hand. For several minutes he didn't react. But then, suddenly, his eyes moved in my direction, and with his eyebrows raised, he fought for focus. It was as if he were walking through a blinding blizzard, dressed only in a tee-shirt, and finally recognized me on the road trying to wave him down. When he saw me, the grimace on his face relaxed, and the curve of his mouth transformed into a smile. A dopey, rubber grin, a kind of drunken smile, but a smile nonetheless. Nate was happy to see me.

Recently I'd arrived at my uncle's house and found him asleep. I'd stood by his bedside debating whether to rouse him. I nudged him gently and he didn't stir. I cleared my throat. Finally I squeezed his shoulder. "Honey, is that you?" he finally said, uncertain until he put his glasses on. Then he smiled with relief. "Oh, I had the nicest nap. But I was sleeping so soundly I think I'd already died. I had to come back from the dead to wake up." We both laughed. There was something so reassuring about the notion of a trial run, of a dying that could be rehearsed.

In my uncle's smile now at his deathbed, an image from his childhood came to me. A family photo that could never have been taken: he's four years old, driving the cobalt blue pedal car his father gave him. Driving in circles, around and around, smiling that same goofy smile. Nate's father sent the pedal car shortly after the divorce to let Nate know he still loved him. Feeling vengeful, his mother took him into the kitchen so that he could see the pedal car but held him back by the shoulders. "He only gave it to you to spite me," she said. "So that good-for-nothing *shicher* could look like a hero when he's not even paying child support." Rebecca never let Nate have the car; she put it out with the rubbish.

The pedal car took on symbolic importance after that. It was the parcel of land on the Las Vegas strip that Nate could have had for a song in 1960, the 50,000 shares of IBM stock he should have grabbed, the girlfriend in Germany he abandoned after the war. "How could I bring a Deutsche girl home to my mother? A Catholic girl whose brother had been in the German army? *Gotynu*. How could I marry her?"

Nathan lived his life in the shadow of the one that got away – the pedal car, the German bride, the final ace, his father. So he'd always had to have something on the side – a girlfriend in addition to a wife, a way around the rules, an escape clause, an inside tip.

But now, on the brink of losing it all, it was if, for a moment, he got it all back. This was heaven for my uncle, I thought, if he could be suspended for eternity in this moment of pedaling his pedal car and basking in his father's love.

"I'm here with you, Uncle Nate," I said.

By the next instant the smile on my uncle's face had eroded, and, as I watched, the familiar face of my grandmother in her final days passed through my uncle's. He hadn't looked so much like his mother in life, but now dying, for an instant, he looked just like her.

"It's Rebecca – " I started to say to Paul, but before I could get the words out the resemblance vanished. Then Nathan looked like no one I'd ever seen, his skin yellow and waxen, with one popped out bluish cheek. His forehead pulled back unnaturally, his teeth jutted out, all the parts of his body disassembling and fragmenting. "Just give us air," they screamed. "Just give us air."

"Why does he have to look like that?" I asked.

"People dying stop looking like themselves," Maureen said. "He's letting go of the body. That's good."

Maureen heard yet another tonal shift.

"Okay, it's time," she said. "Who's ready to do this with me?" Paul, Maureen, and I gathered around the head of my uncle's bed. My brother blessed my uncle again in Hebrew.

"Go toward the light," my brother said. "Go toward the light." I tried to do what the occasion called for but my words sounded lackluster. "Go with your father and mother – they're waiting for you," I said. The very notion of this reunion felt preposterous. My grandfather and grandmother had been estranged from each other for all those years in life, so why would they be together now? I didn't know where in this happy family grouping to place my father either. Nate's feelings about him varied from love to hate, according to the day, sometimes according to the hour, so I just left him out.

Nate was holding his breath in between breaths. And something smelled bad. Had he filled his diaper? Were toxic byproducts released by dying? Maureen applied the blood pressure cuff and listened. "His BP's only 70/40," she said. Beaming. With pride? Satisfaction? His easy dispatch was her accomplishment; it meant she had done her job well.

"The struggle's gone," she said. "See how peaceful it is?"

Peaceful was not the word I would have used. His hands clawed at the sheet. He was still shaking. So was I, nearly as hard as he was.

"There's nothing to be afraid of," Maureen said. The shaking was involuntary, in my body, a sympathetic reaction. I just wasn't made to be standing by and calmly watching this, I thought. Everything in my constitution called for me to wail, gnash my teeth, tear my flesh, howl, resist, protest. Do what a four-year-old would do on separation from her sole protector. Yet some equal force inhibited me from expressing the horror I felt. This was my uncle, my flesh and blood, his skin, his heart, his lungs, his radiant blue eyes, all of which I loved, and he was being wrested away, transformed, while I could only stand by and watch. I thought I might implode. I thought his death might explode out the top of my head or the bottom of my feet.

No wonder my father went crazy when his mother died. How could we not all go crazy? How could we not be crazy all the time? How could we believe in the illusion of security when we had nothing but the loss of those we loved and then – THIS – to look forward to? None of this was Maureen's fault and yet, watching her standing there with a look of serenity on her face, I wanted to tear my uncle's hospice nurse from limb to limb.

"Why are you so frightened?" Maureen said.

What Maureen didn't know is that I've always been afraid of everything – life, death, illness, abandonment, change, loss, having a body, the prospect of not having a body, but now running through what I felt, I recognized that fear was not the dominant feeling. The dominant feeling was nausea. I wanted to throw up. Not only everything I'd eaten that day, that week, I wanted to throw up everything I'd ever eaten. I wanted to throw up my own fleshliness. My uncle's distorted, contorted, grotesque, bad-smelling state disgusted me. I felt the primal disgust of the living for the dead.

"I don't fear death," I said. "I just hate it."

"Move in closer," Maureen said. "We're about to hear his last breaths." Nathan was beyond the point where he could gather strength from our presence – listening for his final breaths could only be fetishistic. We held our breaths and leaned in over the bed. What was left of my uncle took one round-mouthed gasp, and then one more, and froze in mid-inhalation, mouth open, eyebrows strained. His face immediately took on an even more yellow, waxen cast; as far gone as he'd been, yet another transformation occurred when he died.

My brother Paul sighed and walked across the room, crying and shaking as hard as I was. What united us now had nothing to do with faith or faithlessness; it was an animal response to the death of a loved one. Perhaps my brother's ramblings about the soul and my preoccupation with the bodily details served the same function of defending us against the grief that fully felt would overwhelm us. I wanted to hug Paul, to join together in grief, but the total weight of our history stopped me.

I circled around my uncle's dead body, looking for signs that death had brought release. I wished his hands would unclench, his eyelids shut. "Can't we at least close his mouth?" I asked. "We'd have to stitch it shut now," Maureen answered.

At least that awful rattling sound was over, and something did feel lighter in the room. The stillness emanated from him, expanded into the space around him. It wasn't the stillness of an object, not the stillness of the bottle of pills on his night table that he wouldn't need anymore, nor the inanimance of a vase on a shelf. The freezing-in-motion that comes over what was once alive feels different from the stillness of objects. This stillness drew me in, transfixed me. Dead, my uncle no longer repelled me. If it didn't feel like peace exactly, it was something like peace.

* * *

Two months after my uncle died, I had this dream: I find a message on my voicemail, my uncle's voice telling me he's not really dead. "Meet me somewhere," he says. "You may not recognize me because I'll be in a different form, and we're going to have to resume our relationship on a slightly altered basis." There's something creepy and sexually seductive about the rendezvous he proposes. Maybe it's not him, I think, but someone else impersonating him. I try to get other family members to listen to the tape. Somehow in the logic of the dream, my Uncle Nathan is among them. I keep asking him to listen to the tape and verify whether the voice is authentic, to tell me whether I should go to the meeting. But he can't help me. He's sleeping and won't wake up.

Dustin Beall Smith

NO FEELING OF FALLING

From my current perspective as a college professor, it startles me to remember that in the autumn of 1958, after nine weeks of binge drinking, class cutting, and compulsory ROTC drills, I blew off my first semester of college and took a train back east to live with my parents and two younger siblings in a small town forty miles north of New York City. I announced to my family that I had become an existentialist. In what I see now as penance for wasting my father's money, I refused to reoccupy my upstairs bedroom and chose instead to camp on a thin straw mat in a corner of the basement. There I would sit in half-lotus for hours at a time, reading Camus and Kierkegaard, drinking strong Darjeeling tea, and smoking unfiltered Chesterfields. My mother, delighted that I was reading philosophy, encouraged me to read aloud long sections of Sartre's *Being and Nothingness* while she cooked dinner. My father, on the other hand, seemed to take my new philosophical assertiveness as a threat. When I informed him, for instance, that free love was the cool new thing, he told me, "It might

---

Dustin Beall Smith's essays have appeared in *The Gettysburg Review*, *The New York Times Magazine*, *The Sun*, and *Writing on the Edge*. His book, *Key Grip: A Memoir of Endless Consequences*, will be published by Houghton Mifflin later this year.

interest you to know that your mother and I kicked up our heels a time or two before you were born."

Yeah, right, I thought.

My reading had primed me to defy the ticky-tacky, appliance-happy, postwar American zeitgeist. I aspired to and embraced the Beat life – the rebellious, angst-ridden celebration of rootless America – but the family nest gave me little to rebel against. My father made a comfortable living as a commercial artist. My mother was an artist and a homemaker. They each had private studios on the four-acre property. The nineteenth-century house, decorated with their paintings, lithographs, sculptures, and drawings, exuded an atmosphere of creativity and taste. They owned only one car and hardly any modern appliances. The house had no shower, just two small bath-tubs. We almost never watched TV, and dinner table discussions resembled seminars, with subjects ranging from presidential politics (Ike shouldn't have beaten Adlai a second time) to art (photography threatened to replace the canvas) to sports (could anyone ever top that Willie Mays catch?).

This engaged family atmosphere, and my father's seemingly effortless work-at-home lifestyle, created a problem. I needed him to be a weary, briefcase-toting commuter who went to work in a gray flannel suit every day, and because he wasn't, I was forced to respond to his constant presence in a rude and petulant way that betrayed, with its clumsy resentment, an underlying love and admiration. Clearly he was leading an enviable life, but I had no clue how he had arrived at it.

After I dropped out of college, I saw that my hard-won life experience – two high school summers spent mimicking Kerouac by hitchhiking back and forth across the country, holding an assortment of odd jobs, hopping freight trains, and getting jailed for vagrancy – had no value on an adult résumé. I was supposed to get a real job now, but the jobs available to high school graduates did not square with my romanticized self-image. How could a Beat existentialist stoop to working as a clerk at Macy's? I needed a guide to the real world, but my father knew nothing about résumés, personnel agencies, or help-wanted ads. My mother might as well have been living in the nineteenth century. The youngest child of a stock broker, she had never held a full-time job outside the home.

It didn't help that, having been sent away to private school on a scholarship at age fourteen, I knew almost no one in my home town. My former classmates, most of them from New York City and Boston, had all gone off to college, where, unlike me, they remained. My high school girlfriend lived in New York City, only an hour's train ride away, but with my confidence gone, my libido was in hiding. I simply couldn't get off my mat to go see her.

Every night, I assured my parents that the next day I would catch the first train to New York City and ship out to Europe on a freighter, as I had been threatening to do for months. I could count on my mother to respond kindly: "I know you will, dear." But not my father. Though he made few trips into New York himself – and then only to visit the major museums – he pressed me daily to "buckle down and do it."

"I'm going tomorrow, Dad. Take it easy."

"Where have I heard *that* before?" he would ask. "You said the same thing yesterday! And the day before."

"Don't worry, man," I would tell him. "I've scoped it out. I'm going tomorrow."

It got so that I even convinced myself: *tomorrow* I would do it. But every morning, I would wake up with a terrible sinking sensation and go right back to sleep. I developed a persistent headache. One day dragged into the next and a new year rolled around. I couldn't sleep, and I could make no sense of my waking life. I'd been eighteen years old for nine months, legally adult and free, but I couldn't get out of the basement.

Then, one evening in late January 1959, after I'd been home for three months, my father ventured into the cellar. He seemed more upbeat than usual, or maybe less pained at the sight of me. He wore a sweater and slippers and clenched a lit pipe between his teeth. Approaching my straw mat with the prudence of a lion tamer, he tossed me the most recent issue of *The New Yorker*, folded open to the "Profiles" page.

"This might be an interesting avenue of approach," he said. Without waiting for my response, he returned upstairs to have an evening cocktail with my mother. I stared at the article, titled "No Feeling of Falling." A crudely drawn illustration depicted a broad-shouldered man wearing a football helmet, bubble goggles, and two parachutes – one on his back and a smaller one on his chest.

Grudgingly I read the first two sentences: "Jacques André Istel, a twenty-nine-year-old French-American with a Princeton education and a distinguished family background of banking and international finance, is the nation's leading parachutist. It is scarcely too much to say that Istel *is* the parachute movement in the United States."

I stood up from my mat and went upstairs to sit on the living room sofa, where the light was better for reading. My sister and brother, when they saw me, began laughing and playing chopsticks on the piano, but I hardly noticed their antics. I learned that Jacques Istel lived with his beautiful wife, Claudia, and his business partner, Lew Sanborn, in a secluded twenty-seven-room hilltop mansion in Bedford, New York, a town that just happened to be only four miles down the road. The writer pointed out that, despite Istel's family wealth, he had gained real-world experience by hitchhiking, working odd jobs, and getting into trouble. His thirst for adventure had proved nearly inexhaustible, leading him as a youth into all sorts of delinquent and attention-getting behavior. (At age nine, while playing a game he called "bombardier," he broke all 175 panes of glass in his uncle's greenhouse.) He later became a Marine Corps lieutenant in Korea, and in recent years, a combination of rebelliousness and fastidious discipline had propelled him past many obstacles, to a position of prominence in the international parachuting world (whatever *that* was).

As I continued to read, my headache went away and I felt unusually alert. The thirteen-page profile alluded to the military aspects of parachuting and to international parachute competition, and it portrayed the United States as fertile ground for this as-yet-unrecognized sport. The profile writer, Robert Lewis Taylor, concluded that Istel "feels that he is exploring a vast and silent new medium, the deep blue well of the sky, and who knows what may come of it?"

I stood up from the sofa, my head suddenly clear, and joined the family for dinner, then asked my father for the keys to the car.

It is characteristic of all propitious relationships that the moment of first contact seems, in retrospect, inevitable. It happens with love, and it happens with apprenticeships.

It was bitter cold that late January night when I drove to the neighboring town of Bedford. My father had described what he felt sure was the entrance to Istel's property – a nondescript and narrow macadam driveway marked by a battered black mailbox – a few miles east of town. I found the driveway with no problem. Icy in spots, it wound, snakelike, up a very steep and heavily wooded hillside, and broke out suddenly into a cul-de-sac directly in front of Istel's stone mansion. I parked my father's two-door Chevy between a vintage Bugatti racecar, partially covered with a tarpaulin, and a Mercedes 300-SL convertible. A green Volkswagen Bug and a '57 Ford station wagon were parked in front of the garage.

I killed the headlights and waited for guard dogs to bark, but nothing broke the silent darkness surrounding the mansion. When a first-floor light came on, I stepped out of the car, took one last hit off my cigarette, and blew smoke at the stars. Leaving my ski cap and coat in the car, I walked to the front door.

It opened just as I was poised to knock.

I had expected someone other than Jacques André Istel to come to the door, but there he stood in khaki pants and a white T-shirt, looking just as "simian" as *The New Yorker* profile had described him: jet black hair, hunched shoulders, jaw and neck thrust forward, as if he were some great ape about to beat his chest at a challenger. A normal person might have recoiled, but I was no normal person that night. Perhaps that's why I ignored his hostile affect and took a cue from his expression, which seemed both challenging and hopeful, as if he had all along expected someone to show up on his doorstep at just this time of night, though he wasn't yet willing to grant that I was that person.

"What is it you want?" he asked, his French accent stronger than I had imagined.

"I want to make a parachute jump," I said, rubbing my bare hands together.

Istel chuckled. "Hey, Lew!" he called over his shoulder. I looked beyond Istel, into the wide but completely bare foyer – no furniture or art of any kind – and watched Lew walk jauntily toward the door. He had a pleasant face – smooth-browed, soft, and as wholesome as a Midwestern farmer's – and a welcoming smile.

"Look what the cat dragged in," said Istel.

"Yeah," said Lew, "I see!" He held out his hand to me. "Lew Sanborn."

I said my name and shook his hand, then belatedly shook Istel's.

I stood there shivering while Istel launched into a lengthy description of his plans to open the first sport parachuting center in the United States. I hadn't expected a sales pitch, but I listened politely. When Istel was finished, both men stood there staring at me, Sanborn apparently amused by my impulsive late-evening visit.

"We're going to open the center in May," said Istel, his lower jaw thrust forward, as if he were trying to retain a mouthful of water even as he spoke.

"Sounds good," I said, "but when can I make a jump? I might not be around in May."

"Are you looking for work?" Istel asked.

"Yeah," said Sanborn, "are you looking for work?"

Unprepared for the question, I stammered that I was just about to ship out on a Scandinavian freighter headed for a port in Europe. "Going to Brooklyn tomorrow," I said. "Probably ship out within the week. Might be gone a year or two. Don't know."

"Really?" said Istel.

"Hey, that's great," said Sanborn. "A year or two!"

They were toying with me, I could tell, but I didn't let on that I knew. I figured it was a test of some kind.

"Yep," I said. "Just about to ship out. So . . . when can I make a parachute jump?"

"How much does that pay – working on a freighter?" asked Sanborn.

I'd heard rumors that apprentice seamen on non-union freighters earned two dollars and fifty cents a day. "Two-fifty a day," I said. "Plus room and board, obviously. Since it's a freighter."

"Obviously," said Istel, looking at Sanborn and nodding.

"Obviously," said Sanborn, nodding at Istel. "Since it's a freighter."

"Okay," said Istel. "Two dollars and fifty cents a day – that's what we'll pay you." He extended his hand to shake on the deal.

I hesitated. Did he think I was that much of a sucker? I could make two-fifty an *hour*, even without a college degree.

"Plus room and board, of course," said Sanborn, holding a finger up to Istel's face, as if he'd suddenly become my agent. "And the jumps are free, remember that."

"Of course," said Istel, his hand still extended. "You won't get rich working for us," he added "but I'll guarantee you that if you work hard and stick with us, you'll make a name for yourself and have a great time doing it."

He had me. We all shook hands again. And with that, they moved aside and invited me in.

Two days later, at the wheel of Istel's green Volkswagen Beetle, I headed north on a mission to tack up parachuting posters in restaurants, ski centers, and college dorms all over New England. Because I had attended boarding school in southern Vermont, I was familiar with most of the ski centers, the roads, and how to negotiate them in winter (no interstates then). My itinerary would take me straight up to Mont Blanc in Quebec, back down through Vermont, with stops at Stowe, Sugarbush, and Killington, and then east into the White Mountains of New Hampshire, where I'd hit Dartmouth College and Tuckerman's Ravine. Istel fronted me cash for expenses and Sanborn loaded the Beetle with two boxes full of bright orange posters announcing the May opening of the Orange Sport Parachuting Center, in Orange, Massachusetts. The artfully painted posters depicted a single-engine airplane silhouetted against a white sun. Beneath the plane, a spread-eagled skydiver fell into empty space. JUMPED YET? IT'S GREAT! read the bold-face copy. It was the most provocative advertisement I'd ever seen, even more challenging than the war bond posters my father had painted during World War II. One of his had depicted three children standing in the shadow of a Nazi swastika. Don't Let That Shadow Touch Them, it warned. That dark challenge had been met. Now it was time for a new adventure, a new test of will. And where better to go than up?

Along with the posters, I carried two main parachutes and a chest-mounted reserve chute. I also packed white coveralls, a pair of thick-soled Corcoran boots, a white football helmet, and bubble goggles.

"Anyone asks," Sanborn had said, "just suit up and give them a full-gear demonstration."

I could not imagine giving such a demonstration to a stranger, especially since I had never even been in a small airplane, much less jumped from one. But neither could I wait to try on the gear. I spent the first night in Putney, Vermont, at the home of a former teacher. It snowed the next day and took me eight hours to get into Canada. When a snowplow almost buried the car, I pulled off the main highway just a few miles south of Montreal and stopped at a little roadside establishment called L'Auberge something-or-other. The snow banks in the parking lot were ten feet high.

"How much for a single room?" I asked the middle-aged woman at the reception desk.

"*Vous êtes seul?*" she asked.

"What?" I asked.

"You are alone?" she asked again, apparently disgusted by the need to speak English. Heavy bell-shaped earrings stretched her earlobes to the limit; gravity tugged at her fleshy cheeks.

"Yes," I said. "A single room, please."

She looked at me with suspicious, mascaraed eyes.

The room rate did not conform to my strict expense budget, but I had no choice. I signed the register and proudly noted my professional affiliation as "Parachutes Incorporated, U.S.A." The woman issued me the room key, and pointed to an interior hallway just off the lobby.

"No outside entrance?" I asked, illustrating my question with hand gestures.

"*Comment?*" she asked. She smelled of tobacco and talcum powder.

"Never mind," I said.

I unloaded the car and carried everything – parachutes, kit bags, posters – through a set of glass doors, into the motel lobby, and down a long hall to my spacious room. It took me four or five trips, each step monitored by the huffy proprietor. I dumped everything on the bed. After parking the car, I bought a Coke and some peanuts in the lobby and went to my room, eager to be alone with the equipment.

I stripped off my outer garments, and stepped into the jump suit, buttoning it up to the neck. Next, I put on and laced up the spit-polished jump boots, the tops of which came to my midcalves. I pulled heavy rubber bands over the boots, and bloused the cuffs of the coveralls, military style. I stood up, two inches taller in cushioned soles, and admired myself in the large mirror above the dresser.

"Not bad," I said out loud.

I took the free fall parachute from its kit bag and arranged the harness. Then onto my shoulders I heaved it, like a thirty-pound dinner jacket. Sanborn had told me this particular parachute design was an example of the latest technology – something the U.S. Army was just itching to get its hands on. Gone was the old central release mechanism used in World War II. On this chute, the chest and leg straps each had a foolproof quick-release buckle, and the canopy lines could be jettisoned easily if you were being dragged along the ground in a high wind.

I had rehearsed all this information on the drive north. Now that I was actually suiting up, it began to make sense. Watching myself in the mirror, I tightened the straps, stowing the excess under a special elastic cover provided for that purpose. I snapped the reserve chute to two D-rings on the front of the harness and cinched the whole business tight to my body. I put on the bubble goggles, donned the football helmet, and snapped the chin strap. The smell of dry silk and the linseed stink of canvas made me feel brave.

Completely outfitted, I gazed in the mirror. Captivated by the person I saw standing there, as I had been mesmerized by photographs and paintings of soldiers when I was a boy, I felt like a man about to pass through a turnstile into some mythic world. It would be easy to underestimate the significance of that moment – pass it off as adolescent posturing – but I think it was precisely then that two energies began to interact within me: desire and will. By desire I don't mean a conscious wanting, as in wanting to be free and heroic, but rather an ill-defined longing – like that of Narcissus – for some satisfactory reflection of myself. And by will, I simply mean *intent*. I did not have to decide anything. As I stared at myself in the mirror, longing was transformed miraculously into intent. It didn't matter that I hadn't jumped yet. At that moment, I had no doubt at all that I would. The proof stood right there in front of me. The commitment was already made. A feeling of warmth spread through my solar plexus, as if I had just swallowed hot soup. I was going to shake off the curse of the college dropout – and escape what I perceived at the time to be my father's limited world. Soon I would be testing the rarefied air of the parachutist.

Only a handful of Americans jumped out of airplanes for fun in those days. Air-to-air free fall photography did not yet exist. *What would it feel like,* I wondered, *falling all alone through space, free and entirely on my own?* "Like lying on a mattress of air," Istel had said, "no feeling of falling at all."

I could only barely imagine free fall, but I had no trouble envisioning the reputation that would result from such an adventure. Shamelessly, I held an interview with the press right then and there in the motel room. I positioned myself in profile to the mirror, so that I could glance occasionally at the handsome fellow in the glass and admire his strawberry blond hair and his intense blue eyes. I began addressing a very pretty female reporter who just happened to pick me for a private interview and who chose for some inexplicable reason, to sit cross-legged on the end of the bed, pencil in hand, notepad resting on her otherwise bare knee.

"Am I ever scared?" I said, shooting her a cocky grin. "Well, not scared, exactly. But a modicum of apprehension is healthy when you're jumping from a height of twelve thousand feet or so. After all, you're plummeting toward the earth like a rock. At higher altitudes, lack of oxygen complicates the situation . . . Why, yes, actually, I do. I'm glad you ask. I feel it is important that young people have a challenge such as this, but it is not for the faint of heart, as you can imagine . . . Afraid of heights? Me? . . . Do they always send such pretty reporters to cover international championship events like this? . . . Am I free for dinner? You mean tonight? Should we maybe fool around first?"

Just then there came a loud knock on the door. I froze. "Just a minute!" I shouted, ripping off my helmet and bubble goggles. I began frantically loosening the reserve chute tie-downs. But it was too late. The proprietor, using her own key, opened the door. She gasped when she saw me.

"*Je le savais!*" she screamed.

"What?" I said.

"*Vous n'êtes pas seul!*"

"What?"

Her breast heaved and her gullet trembled. "You are not alone! I knew this!"

"What do you mean?" I asked.

"I hear you talking to her! *Je le savais!* Where is she?"

I couldn't decide which was worse, getting caught harboring an unpaid guest or talking to an imaginary woman.

"Who?" I asked.

The proprietor yanked open the closet door, then tore back the shower curtain. She even got down on all fours and peered under the bed.

"I'm alone!" I protested. I started to explain that I was rehearsing for a part in a movie, but she stood up and stomped out before I could finish.

"Really, it's true!" I called after her. "I *am* alone!"

I was not alone, of course. Not really. You can't be self-conscious and alone at the same time. I turned to the mirror again, my heart pounding with shame, my confidence shaken.

Two weeks later, when Istel and Sanborn sent me to live in Orange, Massachusetts, in a rundown farmhouse on the edge of Orange Municipal Airport, I felt as if I'd been assigned to paradise. Already living in the house were Nate Pond and his father, Sebastian "Batch" Pond. Nate, a twenty-seven-year-old Cornell graduate who had recently become a third partner in Parachutes Incorporated, was well on his way to becoming what my father would have called a "rough customer." What struck me right away was the glint in his eye – at once playful and angry – and his restless staccato laugh. His father was both a gentleman farmer and a pilot. As a young man, Batch had flown the mail in Mexico. He liked his vodka and kept cases of it under his bed. Nate didn't seem to have fallen very far from the tree, though he favored beer. I was assigned the smallest room in the farmhouse. When I got out of bed in the morning, my knees touched the wall. But it was better than the basement at home.

In the late 1950s, western Massachusetts was a region in precipitous decline, following the departure of the textile industry after the war. The town of Orange, though nicely situated in the foothills of the Berkshires, felt unprosperous and dreary. It reminded me of the coal mining town in *How Green Was My Valley*, the first movie I saw as a child. Aubuchon's Hardware on Main Street was the place to be during the day, and you had a choice of three establishments in the evening: Frank's Bar, which featured pickled eggs and fifteen-cent glasses of draft beer; the smoke-choked Orange Diner, where you could get a pretty good meatloaf dinner for a couple of bucks; or the upscale DiNapoli's Ristorante, where you could dine in candlelit booths, complete with red-checkered tablecloths, and be served by the owner's sultry, olive-skinned daughter.

I'd come to view devastated towns like Orange through rose-colored glasses – oh, glorious, rootless America! Since I'd never had to live for any length of time in such a place, I was free to admire decay and ignore the misery of the working poor and unemployed. Beneath my romantic view of poverty lay a thinly disguised arrogance born of privilege. I had a developer's eye long before I learned to distrust the process of gentrification that has transformed so many American towns and cities; everywhere, broken down brick buildings, non-functioning watermills, and peeling picket fences resonated with potential. It helped, of course, that I was an advance scout for what would become a noisy invasion of skydivers – one followed closely by reporters and filmmakers. I was riding a gust of fresh air that would very soon put the town on the map.

We began building the jump center in February, when Lew Sanborn arrived from Bedford, bringing his expertise in carpentry and construction. We cleared out the large Quonset-style hangar, erected a wall of parachute storage bins, built six long parachute packing tables, and suspended a parachute canopy simulator from the I-beams. Next to the hangar, we converted a little wooden building into a classroom and installed thirty antique flip-top desks (complete with ink pots), a portable projection screen, and a rolling blackboard. Sometimes, during coffee breaks, I would light a cigarette and scribble in chalk cryptic messages on the blackboard, like *Cogito ergo sum*, or, *Beware the philosophical implications of the transcendence of the ego*. Nate would snort with contempt. "You asshole! That's why erasers were invented."

We dumped a truckload of sand near the flight line, then smoothed it out and set up a water-filled fifty-gallon drum to serve as a platform for practicing parachute landing falls (PLFs). We designed and constructed a mock-up of a Cessna 182, so students could learn the feel of the open door and rehearse aircraft exits.

Istel had leased Orange Municipal Airport from the Town of Orange for twenty years, in exchange for building an aircraft hangar, on the condition that if Russia invaded America, the airport would revert to its intended purpose as a military evacuation facility. Along with three five-thousand-foot runways, the federal government had built a modern administration building, complete with plate glass windows, Unicom radio, weather indicators, multidirectional loudspeakers, and a large wind sock. Not to mention some pretty nice indoor restrooms and a generous reception area. The large parking lot seemed tailored for our arrival, and, just as Istel had envisioned it, high octane gas was available and would attract the pilots of multi-engine planes, along with wealthier clientele.

By early March, all the planes and vehicles were painted blue and white, and we had stenciled Istel's company logo everywhere. I began bulldozing a drop zone in the overgrown triangle formed by the intersecting runways. In the evenings – every evening except Sunday, when nothing was open – Lew, Nate, Batch, and I would hit one of the eating establishments and then close Frank's Bar. It's hard to imagine, at this remove, how delicious a pickled egg tasted when seasoned with salt and washed down with a glass of flat Pabst Blue Ribbon draft beer. Perhaps it's less hard to imagine why, instead of buckling down to college life, I preferred coming in from the winter wind after a hard day's work and hanging out with grown men who talked about dangerous things.

Every single night, after listening to tales of bravery and foolishness, and after nearly choking with laughter about close calls and fatal jumps, I would ask Lew or Nate, "So, when can I jump?" "Maybe tomorrow, if it clears up," Nate would say. Lew reminded me that the air got two to three degrees colder for every thousand feet of altitude. "Soon. Soon."

For weeks on end, I acted like one of the men, singing stupid military songs, falling backwards in unison off barstools, and arm wrestling, but I still couldn't claim to be one of them. I'd been working in Orange for two months, swaggering in front of townspeople, the way I had postured in front of the motel mirror – and answering their questions with the same empty authority I'd displayed for my imaginary reporter in Montreal. Yet I still hadn't jumped. It began to eat at me: what if I chickened out when the time came? Would I freeze like the airborne jumper Lew told me about, whose knuckles had to be pried loose from the door? That guy was screaming like a baby when they tossed his ass out of the plane. Or, worse, what if I froze and they didn't even throw me out of the plane, but just brought me back down and said it was okay? Where could I possibly go after *that*? The tension grew until it was nearly unbearable.

Then, one balmy day in late March, while we ripped eight-foot lengths of tempered masonite through a table saw, Lew suddenly killed the power and asked Nate, "What do you think, should we get it over with?"

"If we have to," growled Nate, taking off his leather nail belt and throwing it on the tarmac. "Goddammit! I guess we have to, right?"

"I mean, we might as well," said Lew, looking exasperated.

"Get what over with?" I asked.

"I mean if we don't, he'll be nagging us right up to opening day," said Lew.

"Pain in the fucking ass," said Nate, spitting a long stream of tobacco juice onto the tarmac.

"If we do it now," said Lew, "maybe he'll shut up and we can get some work out of him."

"Fucking college boys," said Nate, as if he'd never been one himself. "Always nagging. Should draft his ass, send him to Fort Bragg. That'd shut him up."

"Shut who up?" I asked, removing my own nail belt. But I knew who, and I could feel a knot tightening in my stomach.

"We'll give him that old beat-up white canopy," said Lew.

Nate grinned. "You mean the one I used when I jumped in Czechoslovakia? The one that knocked me unconscious when it opened? Good idea!"

"Either that or the one we took off that dead guy – the one who creamed in down at Stormville. You cleaned the blood off it, right?"

"Sure did," said Nate. "Fucking college boy. I'm getting hungry. Let's get this over with."

"Hey," said Lew, "looks like Batch is already warming up the plane! I'll help him take the door off." He winked at me before he walked away.

"Go over there and get up on that oil drum," ordered Nate.

Suddenly, I didn't want to be alone with Nate Pond. I wanted Lew to be my jumpmaster, kind-hearted Lew.

"Do I look like I've got all day?" asked Nate. "Come on, goddammit."

I leapt onto the oil drum and stood there.

"Now put your hands up over your head, like you're holding the parachute suspension lines," said Nate. "Good. Now jump off sideways and do a PLF."

I leapt sideways into the air and landed with my feet together in the sand. The momentum caused me to fall onto my left side, and it carried my feet over my head so that I ended up lying on my right. This absorbed the energy of the fall; I'd been practicing it for months.

"Good," said Nate. "You're ready."

"That's it?" I asked.

"More than I got before my first jump. Fucking Istel. All this pansy-ass training. Come on, get suited up. You already know all this shit."

Ten minutes later, I was sitting on the floor of the Cessna, with my back to the instrument panel, watching Batch adjust the trim tabs after takeoff. I could hardly believe it was finally happening. When I think about it now, from the perspective of a man even older than Batch was back then – when I put myself in the pilot's seat and look down at the kid that was me sitting in the open door – I see a boy struggling with second thoughts. I knew already how to be brave – well, I knew the face of bravery, the affect required – but I also knew too much about the messy consequences of a parachute malfunction. I'd heard a lot of scary jump stories at Frank's Bar. As I gazed down at the sparkling springtime landscape, where newly-melted snow was beginning to pool around yellowing willows, the notorious paratrooper song written to the tune of "Beautiful Dreamer" riffed in my head: "Beautiful streamer, open for me. / Blue skies above, but no canopy."

Just before takeoff, Nate had attached my static line to a D-ring on the floor. As we ascended in a widening spiral above the airport, he double-checked the seating of the ripcord pins on my reserve chute. I experienced a surge of apprehension as I watched his cheeks jiggling in the cold air. My stomach felt suddenly bottomless. We made our first pass over the target at twenty-two hundred feet. Nate determined that because of high winds aloft, my exit point would be more than a mile distant from the drop zone, greatly reducing my chances of hearing instructions from Lew, who was waiting down there to guide me to an accurate landing. We soon climbed to twenty-five hundred feet. Batch banked the plane steeply before leveling out on jump run, and again I felt the bottom drop out of my belly. Apprehension threatened to mushroom into fear, but when I took a deep breath, it subsided. As we passed over the target a second time, I swung my legs out into the wind, positioned myself in the doorway, and looked straight down. I saw Lew, half a mile below, staring up at us, his eyes shaded with his right hand, a bullhorn at the ready in his left.

The plane droned on until all the familiar landmarks passed and bare forest was all that was visible below. After shouting a few last-minute course corrections to Batch, Nate put his hand on my shoulder and yelled that I should reach out and grab the wing strut with both hands. He hollered, "Cut!" Batch throttled back, and the plane seemed almost to buck as it slowed to near stall speed. I placed my left foot on a metal step and my right foot on the landing wheel, and I pulled myself out there in the wind. From my perch beneath the high wing, I glanced over my shoulder at Nate and his father; their mouths were pulled back in identical tight-lipped smiles. Suddenly, it felt perfectly natural that I should kick my feet out behind me and push off with both hands.

It felt right to let go.

With a static line, it takes only three or four seconds before the chute opens. A bright red canopy suddenly blossomed above me, and when I looked down I found myself transfixed by the sight of my own two feet dangling so totally free above the earth. This was me alone up here! Gone was the airplane, gone the obnoxious sound of its engine. Through the ear holes in my football helmet I heard only the flapping of nylon in the breeze. A full minute passed before Lew's amplified voice broke the silence, warning me to turn into the wind to avoid landing in the woods – a precious minute, during which I simply drifted in a self-amazed ecstasy of accomplishment. It was the most intensely private moment of my life up to that time. *If only Dad could see me now!* I thought. I couldn't wait to get down and call my family.

Fifteen months later, in August 1960, a red and yellow bi-plane landed dead-stick on the tarmac, right in front of the airport administration building. Its engine off, the plane touched down silently, bounced once, and then careened wildly between two parked aircraft before screeching to a stop at the gas pumps. A few dozen spectators who had gathered to watch the parachuting let out a collective gasp, as if they'd just witnessed a stunt at some Sunday air show.

Since I was now running the parachuting operation, it was my job to reprimand the pilot. I'd been standing on the flight line, answering some student jumpers' nagging questions about the wind and when it might die down. I excused myself and walked over to the fueling area. With upturned palms, I gave the pilot my best what-the-hell gesture.

"Sorry about that," he yelled. "I plumb ran outta gas!" Craggy-faced and square-jawed, he was wearing a beat-up leather flying helmet and a faded silk scarf. Lifting his oil-spattered aviator goggles, he flashed an appealing grin, completing the iconic image of the outlaw barnstormer. He looked to be about my father's age, but, unlike my father, weather-beaten and rugged. I liked the guy right away. I could tell by the sealed-off front cockpit that the plane, a Stearman, was used for crop spraying. I was not about to hassle a working pilot.

"No problem," I told him.

"Go ahead and top it off," he said.

I gassed up the Stearman, took the pilot's cash, and stood back as he gunned the engine and swung the tail around. At the last minute, I ran over and yelled up to him, "Too bad that front seat's closed off, I'd love to jump out of this beast!" He eased off on the throttle and hollered back, "Get your chute and climb on. I'll take you up right now."

"Climb on?" I asked.

"Right there on the wing. Just watch you don't put your foot through the fabric."

I ran back to my students and told them I was going up to test the wind conditions. "Hang in for a while," I said, grabbing my gear.

A few minutes later the Stearman was roaring along runway three-one, with me lying face down on the lower wing, my arms locked around a diagonal strut. It took nearly the full mile of runway to gather enough speed to clear the trees at the end – my body on the wind-whipped wing had disturbed its natural lift. I had to hang on for a good thirty minutes more before we reached a respectable jump altitude of three thousand feet. My elbows ached and my ribs felt numb from lying on my chest-mounted reserve chute, but when I finally stood up and inched my way forward against the powerful prop blast, I experienced a kind of epiphany – one of those moments it takes a lifetime to digest. Looking down over the leading edge of the bright red wing and seeing the landscape glide beneath me – green New England hills dotted with houses, steeples, and cows – I felt a surge of power so pure and thrilling, so sunlit and masculine, I would draw upon it for years to come. Everything seemed possible. I had earned the future.

In a month, I would leave Orange to begin my first semester at Columbia University. My father had already written the check. I would rent a tiny room near the campus, and New York City would soon swallow me whole. But I didn't know that yet. Just then, I felt decidedly immortal, and when the pilot made a circular gesture with his gloved hand, suggesting we do a back loop, I gave him a heartfelt thumbs-up and hung on for dear life. The earth below disappeared from my view and the sky and sun revolved in a mad crescendo of full-throttled power accompanied by a G-force that nearly buckled my knees.

When the plane leveled, the pilot smiled and jerked his head toward the tail: *Time to get off my wing.* I didn't want to go, didn't want the flight to end. It all seemed so clear from up there. I had discovered the perfect intersection of willingness and opportunity, hidden in an otherwise misty landscape of luck or fate or whatever you want to call the unknown. I could do anything, if I dared.

I pulled myself closer to the engine cowling and inched my way back along the yellow fuselage, careful to step only on the narrow skid-proof surface. "Thanks!" I yelled to the pilot. Then I simply let go, and the wind swept me from the wing like a speck of dust.

Leigh Morgan Owen

THE TRICKY THING ABOUT ENDINGS

I had a dog's sense that day. Maybe from a week camping in the woods, smelling the world, eating wild things, peeing on dirt. Dad was alone in the kitchen. "Who died?" I asked him, still holding my duffle. He answered as though it wasn't a strange question.

"Your mother has cancer."

You and your cancer were walking downstairs to greet me. What was left of my heart, coordinated with my mouth to construct an "everything will be okay" smile. I listened to your steps. I considered tempo. Slower than usual? Faster? What would either mean anyway? Would I recognize a scared step? And what would I do if I did? You came into the kitchen. You looked sheepish, caught with something you shouldn't have. I just looked. We were locked in a moment of nothing to say. So you made tea. Why wouldn't you make tea? It was only cancer then. Then there was some hope.

"The Tricky Thing About Endings" is Leigh Morgan Owen's first publication in a national literary magazine.

I had just turned nineteen and I thought I knew everything. You might think I'd be wiser now. Maybe I've looked back, realized how little I knew then. Or that today I'd say something like, "I know even less, now." But it isn't true. Now I do know everything. I know that all things end. And everything is just an extension of that.

* * *

Six months. That's what they gave you. We had waited in the exam room, sitting on metal stools. You were still. I was gripping my stool, rolling around, pacing on wheels. All day strangers had been analyzing pictures of your insides, pointing and nodding at black spots that looked fine to me. Or was it the white spots they were looking at? But then they stopped.

There's nothing like waiting to hear how long you're expected to live. "Nerve-wracking," is what you called it. I called it a different sort of wait than say, waiting in traffic or waiting to find out if you're blind in one eye. Those only seem important.

The doctor came in, rolled her stool up to us, close. Too close. Still, we rolled forward too, forming a three-person huddle in the center of the room. I wondered: offense or defense? "No point in mutilation tactics," is what she said. That was meant as a bad thing. Three of us now, locked in a moment of nothing to say. This would start happening a lot. You could have chemo, the doctor tells us, handing me a green pamphlet titled, *Advanced Cancer: Living Each Day.* A guidebook, of sorts. Destination: death. She says chemo can't save you, only prolong it. Prolong "it." She didn't specify: life or death. On the cover of the pamphlet was a sketch of an old lady. Your hair was long, blond. Not a single grey. And I didn't even know how young forty-two was then. The doctor advised you to get your affairs in order. There was a "Personal Inventory" form in the pamphlet to help. A to-do list for the road. On the way home, you rode shotgun, guide on your lap. I looked down at it every so often, driving slowly even for the slow lane. When we got home, I saw the tea kettle on the stove and caught the lingering scent of our former life before you went upstairs to clean your closets and I sat and watched.

* * *

Lessons from Advanced Cancer: Living Each Day

"There are no right or wrong ways to face the end of life. We each find our own way to die. We are all born with a will to live. By participating with others you say, 'I care about myself.' You should ask yourself, 'What do I cherish?' Try to live as normally as possible. As cancer progresses, your appearance may change. This may affect your self-respect. If pain reaches the point where it disturbs you, it needs to be treated. Emotions that many people with advanced disease experience have been examined by trained professionals. You may feel depressed. Discussing practical matters now can eliminate many problems."

Personal Inventory. Fill in the blanks.

Name. Blank. Date. Blank. Address. Blank. Date of Birth. Blank. Place of Birth. Blank. Social Security Number. Blank. Next of Kin. Blank. Employer. Blank. Company Benefits. Blank. Personal Papers. Blank. Insurance: Life. Blank. Health. Blank. Automobile. Blank. Company. Blank. Bank Account Number. Blank. Other Accounts. Blank. Automobile (Make, Model, Year). Blank. Real Estate Papers. Blank. Personal Items of Value. Blank. Blank. Blank. Counselors Who Can Help With My Affairs. Blank. Attorney. Blank. Banker. Blank. Insurance Agent. Blank. Doctor. Blank. Clergy. Blank. Other. Blank. Funeral Arrangements. Blank. Blank. Blank. Special Requests. Yes. Stop this.

* * *

After your impromptu closet cleaning, you asked me to cut off all your hair so I did. I had never seen your hair shorter than really long. You must have figured that it was hair that looked great on a head, not all over the house falling out haphazardly from chemo. It was a preemptive strike against needless cleaning like telling us to wipe our shoes before coming into the house. Kind of like that, anyway.

It was thick and the scissors kept getting stuck.
"Let me try," you offered.
"I'll do it," I said, because it was all I could do and because I couldn't watch you do it. But the scene was mostly business since I didn't think anything ended and you knew everything did. I saved some clippings in a paper bag until a few years ago. I never intended on saving them, but once I had them, I felt strange throwing them out. After some time, I felt strange not to.

That's the tricky thing about endings. Even if you know that all things end, it doesn't mean you know *when* something has. It's not until you stop thinking the echoes are the voices. Sometimes you just look back and think, "Oh. That ended."

Now I only have a little, a lock in a locket.

* * *

We didn't know the whole story then. We didn't know "it" would last eight years. I've heard people say, *begin with the end in mind*. But that's how you began each day for eight years and I don't think it was such a great thing.

These days, I begin most of my days with your end in mind too. Now I know your whole story. Someone else will know mine. I wonder what you would think about me writing a memoir. I can't decide if you would be proud or angry. It matters, so I decide you would be proud. It never goes away – the urge to show, to ask, to tell you something. One day I was on the treadmill, a TV bolted in front of me. The news was on, no sound. Men in suits were standing around a large conference table, staring down at something I couldn't make out. One of the men pulled out a ruler, placed it next to the thing and everyone nodded, smiled. I thought it might be a baby animal. It wasn't. It was a mammoth Funyun: an onion-flavored ring grown out of control. This is what you're missing. I would have called you – urgent voice – told you to turn on the news. "Something important is happening," I would have said. I read somewhere that the owner tried to auction the onion ring to raise money for her school band. No takers. I wouldn't have been able to sell it. I would have kept it as long as possible, shellacking it, if I had to. But then, I get attached to things. Someone told me that Frito-Lay wanted to study it to see how mutations happen but wouldn't pay the five dollars for it. Then a friend of hers broke it.

* * *

We became regulars at the clinic in one day. I remember walking past men ripping up brand new carpeting. I asked someone why. A woman told me that several patients had walked in, seen the carpet, vomited. The rug was the same pink as one of the cancer drugs.

I wondered if you could recognize the sound of a scared step. I slowed my pace, raised my voice.

According to the schedule I was given – the one that had the rest of your life planned with fill in the blanks – there wasn't a blank for what I should say to you. It was easiest to say, "What time is the appointment?" "Do you want me to carry that for you?" You always told me, "If you don't have anything nice to say, don't say anything at all."

Is, "Are you afraid to die?" in the nice category? What about, "Do you feel your life was fulfilled?" or "If not, is there anything we can do between now and Monday that will make you feel that it was?" I knew that "How did this happen? Weren't you being tested? Your mother died of this at forty-two. What were you thinking?" were definitely not nice.

Instead, I punctuated everything with "I love you."

"Do you think you're going to be sick? I love you."
"Can I make you tea? I love you."
"What did Dr. Shapiro say about the sore? I love you."

And ten days before, you had been telling me to pick up all my shit from the kitchen table. I wanted to tell you, *I picked it all up, Mom.*

* * *

"You're getting ninety percent of what a person can tolerate in a lifetime," Doctor Shapiro told you. Trial drugs for a Stage IV illness. Stage IV, the final act. The doctor seemed excited to me. I would get used to that. I'd also get used to the pink forms: if you died or were poisoned beyond reason, there is nothing anyone could do about it. You will have nausea, vomiting, mouth ulcers, loss of taste. Your skin might change color. Your urine might too. Oh, and your fingernails. There's likely to be damage to your heart and liver. No more menstruation. And remember, you can't go in the sun. But you'll be too tired anyway, or want to be inside because of the diarrhea. But think of all the people you'll be helping, all the things they'll be learning from your body's mutation. Sign and date here.

I wondered if they were saving that ten percent for later, a curtain call? Were they being cautious? I decided. They were saving it. You were grateful to be helping some other woman who would be going towards "it" in the future. "Go ahead, use me," you told them.

You called it your cocktail. Everyone did. The bar was the infusion room. You were infused on a pink lounge chair. I watched. The recipe was nine parts lethal, one part merely toxic. Too much would kill you and the right amount, the cancer. I reminded you that everything was a poison in the wrong measure: water, vitamins, oxygen. Later, I would add 'people' to the list. I told you I didn't know everything then.

Each infusion, I wondered if the nurse had measured correctly. Was she distracted? Had she fought with her boyfriend the night before? Her kids? Her mother? Just one mistake. And I had thought 'trust' was letting a stranger drive me around in a taxicab.

Your first time getting chemo, I was wedged between you and a girl about my age. I wondered if she had been given the guidebook too. I smiled at her, wishing I hadn't washed my hair. She smiled back, told me she had a brain tumor and a year to live. I think I said, "Oh." I asked her if she needed anything and then felt cruel. But she asked me to get her a Vogue and to give platelets. I did both.

* * *

Take temp. 100° Give you meds. Wait. Vomit? No. Log. Sleep 3 hours. Wake up. Take temp. 100° Give you meds. Wait. Vomit? Yes. Suppository. Log. Sleep 3 hours. Wake up. Take temp. 100° Give you meds. Wait. Vomit? No. Log. Sleep 3 hours. Wake up. Take temp. 103° Get Dad. Pack bags. Drive to hospital. Wait. Fill out form. Then more forms. Come home. Log. Try to sleep. Pretend to sleep. Get up. Get bucket for car. Drive to hospital. Pick you up. Drive home. Give you meds. Wait. Vomit? No. Take temp. 100° Log.

Repeat intermittently for eight years.

Guidebook Lesson: Try to live as normally as possible.

There's nothing like a beautiful day when someone you love is dying. It's like eating candy with a cold. You're certain you like the stuff. You've tasted it before. You see it, your tongue tickles. You put it in your mouth, it feels creamy. Chew it – Nothing. Swallow it – Tasteless. Those days, I would get in my car and drive, windows down, leaving behind the pills, gauze, ooze, reek, pain. Driving in my car, seeing the world, feeling the world's breeze – I wanted to – I tried to – I could – almost – enjoy it. I wished it was guilt that held me back. But I had just lost my taste for a beautiful day. Now I know that's a sign of something ending.

* * *

We moved you to the first floor, a move down, the living room. You wanted the bed in the center. The position seemed odd to me. People could walk around all sides of the bed, viewing from every angle. Like you were an exhibit at The Museum of Mom. I kept offering to move the bed next to a wall. I would have wanted the wall, a solid place to turn. But what comfort would a wall be to you? Enclosure was the last thing you wanted.

It was a practical matter. It was about table space, having everything in arm's reach. On one side, you had pill bottles, gauze pads and kidney-shaped hospital dishes filled with pennies and jewelry that no longer fit. On the other side, lay your wig and some bandanas. And that blue plastic bucket was there too. It was no longer a living room.

It was a room with a view, through pages of books. I had brought you these books from your wish lists of mysteries and travel. I sat on the edge of the bed and listened to you recount the stories to me. I heard them differently than you did. All the travels were still a possibility for me.

Now I have the same view. Your books, in my apartment. I found a tasseled bookmark in one. It says, "The best way to travel is by means of imagination." It marked your travels with Gypsies on their journey from India to Eastern Europe. From the living room, you hitchhiked into the wild of Alaska, spent a quaint year in Provence, and journeyed to the frontiers of anarchy after time in Dublin.

Without you to explain, what do I make of the passages highlighted in Chopin's *The Awakening*?

> *The children appeared before her like antagonists who had overcome her; who had overpowered and sought to drag her into the soul's slavery for the rest of her days*

And

> *"you are burnt beyond recognition," he added looking at his wife as one looks at a valuable piece of personal property which has suffered some damage*

* * *

"I guess you only make drop-offs," you joked to the van driver. Driving someone to a hospice is pretty awkward without humor. You were always trying to help.

Like the day you died. You lifted your head off the pillow, and opened your mouth to say something to me. Nothing came out. You kept trying.

> *say it – say it – say it – say it – say it – say it – say it – say it one more time*

"I know. I love you and you love me Mom. Put your head down."
You smiled, put your head down. Stopped helping.

Someone drove you to the cemetery. No humor. You were just
there one day. So we were too. Me, Dad and Will. And it was an ugly
day so I didn't have to worry.

* * *

Heaven, hell, back to the earth, a better place, with her now, with
him now, with God, a ghost, a soul, a spirit, a banshee, rebirth, rein-
carnation, resurrection now, resurrection later, nothingness, this
world, the next, at peace, at rest, gone. The end.

It's not where you're going that's important. It's where you're not.

Sometimes I drive with my eyes closed. And I accelerate. I thought
everyone did that. I asked my friend, Stephanie, and she told me that
the only time she closes her eyes while driving is to blink. So I asked
Will if he did. He said, "Not in a while."

POETRY

ABOUT THE GUEST POETRY EDITOR

Jane Hirshfield, a contributing editor of *Alaska Quarterly Review*, is the author of six collections of poetry: *After* (finalist for England's T.S. Eliot Award in 2006), *Given Sugar, Given Salt* (finalist for the 2001 National Book Critics Circle Award, and winner of the Bay Area Book Reviewers Award), *The Lives of the Heart*, *The October Palace*, *Of Gravity & Angels*, and *Alaya*, as well as a book of essays on poetry, *Nine Gates*. She also edited and co-translated two poetry anthologies: *The Ink Dark Moon: Love Poems by Komachi & Shikibu, Women of the Ancient Court of Japan* and *Women in Praise of the Sacred: 43 Centuries of Spiritual Poetry by Women*. Her work has appeared in many publications including *The New Yorker*, *The Atlantic*, *The Nation*, *The American Poetry Review*, *Alaska Quarterly Review*, and five editions of *The Best American Poetry*.

David Baker

SECOND TORNADO

This time the porch seems to pitch to the side.
Or is everything else shoved that way? Blown
yellow, yellow-green, leaf chaff in big sheets
flying across the porch hard from the side.
What you hear about the train isn't true.
Yet there are passengers riding the rails
of the wind, larks awing, a wild meadow
variety but more like confetti

than birds, and pages of evening news
in a real hurry. And the gray-green sky
isn't true, unless the flailing hung ferns
like electrocuted dolls are enough
in the sky to count. Now the squad's
streaming the block, on lookout for downed lines.
And now the banging of the porch eaves is
inside the eaves. Now the harder rain –

the first was Kansas, devil-in-the-heat,
yet it lifted shingles off a flat house
and tore the tarpaper, toys in the yard,
then the roof as we watched from the ball field.
She was elsewhere, nobody to me then,
unmet for decades coming on. O
wind. O wild love. Whirl me in the sky
sideways to her now and toss me down.

David Baker's latest books are *Radiant Lyre: Essays on Lyric Poetry* (Graywolf, 2007) and *Midwest Eclogue: Poems* (Norton, 2005).

Chana Bloch

THE SIXTH TRUMPET

after Anselm Kiefer

Lately we've begun to talk logistics,
to draw up contingency plans
for a war we're preparing
to lose. We've begun to count backward

from D-day. *If I die first,* we tell each other.
Sometimes: *If you die first.* Declarations
that flare in the street, the museum.
Our children can't stand that kind of talk,

they announce in front of Kiefer's painting.
They see an immense ploughed field
under a day sky seeded with dark stars.
Sunflower seeds! they say. *He used real seeds.*

We see a bombardment of cinders
falling through the air onto furrows
of emulsion, acrylic, shellac
that converge on a vanishing point.

No place to hide from the sky
– we've got to prepare a shelter
for them. We dole out small truths,
sufficient unto the day.

Sunflower seeds, we say.

Chana Bloch is a poet, translator and literary critic. Among her published works are three books of poems, *Mrs. Dumpty, The Past Keeps Changing,* and *The Secrets of the Tribe,* five books of translation from ancient and contemporary Hebrew poetry, and a critical study of George Herbert.

THE DAILY NEWS

Bellagio, Italy

The Romans were here before us.
Before them the Etruscans.
Before anyone, the slow grind of ice
gouging out sheer rock walls and a lake.

I like the long view back, the boulders
stranded by glaciers in their wake.
Those rocks are solid fact; they're not
going anywhere soon.

Day doesn't settle down long enough
to be seen. Wherever
the eye alights suddenly it's dark.

Yesterday rose and fell in a cloud of ash
and already the augurs are bringing reports
of tomorrow's war.
They're tracking the travel plans of birds.

Yet today: snow flurries in April,
snow-buds on the branches!
We rush out ready to hope, but the sky
turns to water in our hands.

Wherever the eye rests there is light and sorrow,
sorrow and light,
Escher birds, beak-to-wing,
frozen in flight.

Robert Bly

AN ONION

The skin of the onion is shiny as a deerfly's wing, and it echoes the faint blood veins of the eyelid, the Renaissance capillaries one often sees in human skin. A wild greenish-yellow light shows through from the deeper onion. The surface shows dark splotches here and there, clouds moving overhead, darkening patches of the stubble field.

What shall we say of these lines – moving over the vast spaces of the onion – but barely visible, like those curving drawings on the high plains of Peru. The onion lines gradually widen at its center; they catch more sunlight there, glinting with a sort of ruffian, toothy joy; after that they curve down toward the disappointed knot at the bottom. The ruffian lines do grow more succinct as they reach the worried fibers at the bottom. They are like the survival root of the old man, barely able to breathe, who walks with a cane, head down. He's a tough old guy, who doesn't care about you.

Robert Bly is the author of more than thirty books of poetry, including *My Sentence Was a Thousand Years of Joy* (HarperCollins, 2005); *The Night Abraham Called to the Stars* (HarperCollins, 2001); *Snowbanks North of the House* (1999); *What Have I Ever Lost by Dying? Collected Prose Poems* (1992); *Loving a Woman in Two Worlds* (1987); *Mirabai Versions* (1984); *This Body is Made of Camphor and Gopherwood* (1977); and *The Light Around the Body* (1967), which won the National Book Award. Among his many books of translations are *The Winged Energy of Delight: Selected Translations, Lorca and Jiminez: Selected Poems* (Beacon Press, 1997); *Machado's Times Alone: Selected Poems* (1983); *The Kabir Book* (1977); *Friends, You Drank Some Darkness: Three Swedish Poets—Martinson, Ekeloef, and Transtromer* (1975); and *Neruda and Vallejo: Selected Poems* (1971). Bly's nonfiction books include *The Sibling Society* (Addison-Wesley, 1996); *The Spirit Boy and the Insatiable Soul* (1994); *Iron John: A Book about Men* (1990); and *Talking All Morning: Collected Conversations and Interviews* (1980).

WALKING OUT IN THE MORNING

In the city, whenever you walk out,
The air hits you first . . . abundant,
Nonhuman. Where has it been?
It's like your first college course,

But with better teachers. Farther on,
Your legs begin to feel the cold.
And you learn more. It's like
Graduate school, in which

Your shoes keep slipping
On the ice, and you notice
The mountains are getting
Steeper, like those in Germany.

If you keep walking anyway,
You'll have a Ph.D.
You'll know you're near God
When your boots are full of snow.

Thomas Centolella

CREELEY

(1926–2005)

Jackhammers. It must be October.

If the man with the black eye patch were still alive
he might pause in his latest digression,
he might turn to the classroom window and murmur,
"A little something for our attention
to work against." He might return
to his reminiscence of two green poets
making another pilgrimage to the Master
of New Jersey. They sit in Dr. Williams's sun room
like two Boy Scouts hankering after a merit badge.
Or he might meditate aloud on the attributes
of Levertov: "Responsibility is the ability
to offer a *response*," fixing the room's fledglings
with his one good eye. Then maybe
another pause, while he digs deep
for his hanky, flips up the pirate patch
and wipes out the moist hollow nobody wants
to look at. Then off he goes again – the time
he and Famous Name went to Famous Place
and took another step toward celebrity –
until, fidgety with tangent and anecdote,
we pull him back on track because,
one day after class, he said he'd go on
and on if nobody stopped him.
We stopped him – when we could.
He would chuckle, which you could say
was his way of being responsible. . .

Thomas Centolella is the author of three collections of poetry from Copper Canyon
Press, including *Views from along the Middle Way*. He has been the recipient of a Lannan
Literary Award and the American Book Award. This is his second appearance in *Alaska
Quarterly Review*.

A jackhammer shatters the concrete
and I'm staring again at the rheumy cave
of an eye socket. We were good students,
I think. We took on the interruptions
and reinforced our focus.
We looked death in the eye
and didn't blink.

Henri Cole

SUNFLOWER

When Mother and I first had the do-not-
resuscitate conversation, she lifted her head,
like a drooped sunflower, and said,
"Those dying always want to stay."
Months later, on the kitchen table,
Mars red gladiolus sang *Ode to Joy*,
and we listened. House flies swooped and veered
around us, like the Holy Spirit. "Nature
is always expressing something human,"
Mother commented, her mouth twisting,
as I plucked whiskers from around it.
"Yes, no, please." Tenderness was not yet dust.
Mother sat up, rubbed her eyes drowsily, her breaths
like breakers, the living man the beach.

Henri Cole's volumes of poetry include: *Blackbird and Wolf* (Farrar, Straus & Giroux, 2007), *The Visible Man* (2005), *Middle Earth* (2003), which received the 2004 Kingsley Tufts Poetry Award, *The Look of Things* (1995), *The Zoo Wheel of Knowledge* (1989), and *The Marble Queen* (1986).

Greg Delanty

CHILDHOOD

(from *THE GREEK ANTHOLOGY, BOOK XVII*)

You wax lyrical about childhood being idyllic,
   a paradise, Eden, a country under a spell:
a beachball in the air, an uncle with the trick
   of a penny up his sleeve, a lick
of ice cream, blithe waving from the horses of a carousel
   galloping the hills of childhood. Well,
sure, but look again at the impaled horses circling the carousel,
their faces appear as if they're being whipped through hell.

(Danus)

Greg Delanty's *Collected Poems 1986–2006* was recently released from the Oxford Poet's series of Carcanet Press. Other books include *The Ship of Birth* (Carcanet Press 2003, Louisiana State University Press 2007), *The Blind Stitch* (Carcanet Press 2001, Louisiana State University Press 2002) and *The Hellbox* (Oxford University Press 1998).

Carl Dennis

OTHER ANSWERS

Now he's gone off, the middle-aged man
Who rang the doorbell a moment ago
Looking for the Russo family,
And already I'm sorry I settled for saying, "No.
No Russos Here." A true reply,
True to the precept against deception.
But what about a flow of fellow feeling
That would have pushed me to step out
On the porch a moment – pulling a coat on
Against the November chill – and point
To houses where I knew for certain
The man would be wasting his time to ring?
A dinner guest, maybe, growing uneasy
About finding the residence of his new friends.
Am I so gloomy about the likelihood
Of stories with happy endings that I'd like everyone
To stay home, content with his portion,
However meager? Or did the man remind me
Of a character in a play who spells trouble,
A borrower who might bleed a house dry,
A talker so courteous he makes a wife regretful
She didn't meet him before she met her husband.
Or did I suspect he'd envy the pair the joy
Each feels in the other's company, as Iago
Envies the love of Othello and Desdemona?
If I want to be fair, I have to assume the visitor
Innocent until proven guilty. For all I know
He could add to the play the part of the true friend
That Shakespeare hasn't provided, a counterpoise

Carl Dennis is the author of eleven volumes of poetry. His most recent collection is *Unknown Friends*, published by Penguin in 2007. He won the Pulitzer Prize in poetry in 2002.

To the secret enemy. What a difference he'd make
By urging Othello to pause a moment,
Listen, and reconsider. However else
The world would remain the same
If I were inclined to give fuller answers,
Othello's story might be less predictable.
He wouldn't always stumble without a candle
To the final scene, wouldn't always learn late
What he'd give everything to learn earlier.

Sharon Dolin

FOR I WILL CONSIDER THE OVERLOOKED DRAGONFLY

How it is often a damselfly, skimmer, or darner
How it belies the idea that we invented neon
How it mates while in flight, laying eggs on the pond's lilies
How its blues are purples, its browns, reds
How unfearful it is of the human body
How one will come to bask on my forearm, foot, or the arm of my deck chair
How I praise the way it eats the larvae of biting insects
How a Variable Dancer in lavender and black alighted as I wrote this
For I praise them, not needing to search for dragonflies (the way birders search
     for birds) but let them fly to me
For sometimes their wings have stigma and in the wind I watch
     their wings and abdomen sway while their head and thorax are still
For this one's a male whose spider-web wings and abdomen are tipped sky-blue
For might it be the same damselfly that alights on the arm of my chair as I write?
For his bulgy compound eyes, what do they see?
For his violet thorax the color of a flower
For the honeybees grazing the sea honeysuckle
     and the hummingbirds on the mimosa blooms
For their pond world which is oblivious to names
For ours with its naming obsession
For the only way I desire to catch one is with the net of my eyes
For some say a damselfly is a weak flier compared to a dragonfly
For the male clasps the female's head with the end of its abdomen when mating
For we call mating pairs a copulation wheel but I say they look like a backwards 3
For it flies from spring through late summer (though they live for only a few weeks)
For some darters and skimmers migrate south and the ones returning are their
     children or grand- or great-grandchildren or

Sharon Dolin won the 2007 AWP Donald Hall Prize in Poetry for her book *Burn and
Dodge,* to be published by the University of Pittsburgh Press in 2008. She is the author
of three previous books of poems: *Realm of the Possible, Serious Pink,* and *Heart Work.*

For after the storm a male white-faced Meadowhawk, its thorax and abdomen
  pomegranate-red, has come to bask in the windy sun
For the wind, the wind, which causes a stirring within the stillness
  and a stillness within the stirring

Mark Doty

APPARITION

Oracular pear,

this peacock
perched in a plywood roost
at the garden center,

magnificent behind a wire fence
marked with his name:
Hommer

(pronounced
without the extra m),
and hand-lettered instructions:

DON'T PROVOKE ME.

He's the provocation:
of what use
the wrought extravagance

he's not just now displaying?
Darwin: "The sight of a feather
in a peacock's tail,

Mark Doty's new collection, *Fire To Fire: New And Selected Poems*, is forthcoming from HarperCollins in 2008. He is the author of several collections of poetry: *School of the Arts* (HarperCollins, 2005); *Source* (2002); *Sweet Machine* (1998); *Atlantis* (1995), which received the Ambassador Book Award, the Bingham Poetry Prize, and a Lambda Literary Award; *My Alexandria* (1993), which won the National Book Critics Circle Award and Britain's T. S. Eliot Prize; *Bethlehem in Broad Daylight* (1991); and *Turtle, Swan* (1987). He has also published *Heaven's Coast* (1996), which won the PEN/Martha Albrand Award for First Nonfiction. Other books by Doty include *Firebird* (1999), *Still Life with Oysters and Lemon: On Objects and Intimacy* (2000), and *Dog Years* (HarperCollins, 2007).

whenever I gaze at it,
makes me sick!"
No reason on earth

even eons of increments

would conspire to this,
and is the peahen
that hard to attract,

requiring an arc of nervous gleams,
a hundred shining animals
symmetrically peering

from the dark
of ancient woods?
But if Hommer argues

by his mere presence

for creation, his deity's
a little hysteric,
rampant attitude

contained in all that glory.
Did he who made the lamb
make Hommer, imperious

metallic topknot shivering
above an emerald field
of anodized aluminum

while he blinks and flicks

his actual eyes from side to side?
And then the epic
trombone-slide-from-Mars cry

no human throat can mime
– is that why it stops the heart? –
just before he condescends to unfurl

the archaic poem of his tail.

Stephen Dunn

EXCITEMENT

For years I sought it, had it,
the physical kind – visceral
and a little dangerous –
and would try to wear it
like a bright shirt
so that others might recognize
and be drawn to it,
perhaps want,
with my assistance,
to investigate it further.

But I've watched with curiosity
that kind of excitement
slowly give up its spot
at the top of my day,
in effect watched it
learn to play with others,
like its far away cousin,
Contemplation,
like its little known peer,
Emotional Generosity.

Excitement, I might think
to myself on days like today,
and mean something quiet
or tender, or, yes,
passionately quiet and tender,
or maybe even selfish,
and be reminded

Stephen Dunn is the author of fourteen collections of poetry, including *Different Hours*, winner of the 2001 Pulitzer Prize. This is his second appearance in *Alaska Quarterly Review*.

that to redefine is not always
to lose. Astonishing

that sometimes we don't
quite have to kiss
what we've loved goodbye.

Laura Fargas

LIFEWORK

What hard work it is to be the living.
How much easier they have it,
or, to be exact, he has it, the dear departed
slack in his box like a present that,
once the tissue petals were unfolded,
wasn't wanted, like handmade socks
in some unspeakable plaid. Well,
that's okay, just shove this box over
and go on to the next, which might be,
at last, Malibu Barbie or electric
trains. We are gathered to celebrate,
even if the givers got it wrong again –
you think it's going to be a new house,
and it is, a sort of sub-basement
sub-efficiency and they've given you
fee simple absolute, a form of forever
the law calls a *freehold,* though you
paid with your life. And we others
got the flowers and our fancy clothes,
a smoky set from a wind instrument,
food and decent wines whose outer wraps
guarantee there'll be no disappointment.
Of course, we had to buy the wine
ourselves – but that's our work, from
picking the grape to glueing the label,
and in time (which is not the opposite of,
but instead comes before, *out of time*)
we learn to take it up gladly.
Hell, let's celebrate that too, even

Laura Fargas is the author of two books of poetry, *Reflecting What Light We Can't Absorb: Poems* and *An Animal of the Sixth Day.* Her poems have appeared in *The Paris Review, Poetry,* and *The Atlantic.* This is her second appearance in *Alaska Quarterly Review.*

toast the givers, because they once
gave us you, and ourselves, gifts so good
we were willing to pay in blood,
as after all we will, when the piper's final note
comes in its windowed envelope that lets us
see inside and glimpse the bill.

in mem. Bill Matthews

Katie Ford

EARTH, THIS FIRELIT LANTERN

will master the heart
only in its last hour
of wicking down, flickering to light
its own wounds and mishandlings,
what's been taken and what collected
on this extinguishing thing.

You whose love once left
but returned
must forget
your human analogy.

Deadly to believe a heaven
might include you.

You had a heaven.
You were its gods.

Katie Ford is the author of *Deposition, Storm* (a chapbook), and *Colosseum* (Graywolf, 2008). Individual poems have appeared in *The Paris Review, American Poetry Review, Ploughshares, Seneca Review,* and *Poets & Writers.*

Jack Gilbert

DREAMING AT THE BALLET

The truth is, goddesses are lousy in bed.
They will do anything it's true.
And the skin is beautifully cared for.
But they have no sense of it. They are
all manner and amazing technique.
I lie with them thinking of your
foolish excess, of you panting
and sweating, and your eyes after.

Jack Gilbert is the author of *Views of Jeopardy,* winner of the 1962 Yale Younger Poets Series, *Monolithos* (1982), and *The Great Fires* (1994). His collection *Refusing Heaven* (2005), won the 2006 National Book Critics Circle Award and the *Los Angeles Times* Book Prize. His collected poems will be published in 2009.

SOUTH

In the small towns along the river
nothing happens day after long day.
Summer weeks stalled forever,
and long marriages always the same.
Lives with only emergencies, births,
and fishing for excitement. Then a ship
comes out of the mist. Or comes around
the bend carefully one morning
in the rain, past the pines and shrubs.
Arrives on a hot fragrant night,
grandly, all lit up. Gone two days
later, leaving fury in its wake.

NEGLECTING THE KIDS

He wonders why he can't remember the blossoming.
He can taste the brightness of the sour-cherry trees,
but not the clamoring whiteness. He was seven in
the first grade. He remembers two years later when
they were alone in those rich days. He and his sister
in what they called kindergarten.
They played every day on the towering
slate roofs. Barefoot. No one to see them on
those fine days. He remembers the fear
when they shot through the copper-sheeted
tunnels through the house. The fear
and joy and not getting hurt. Being tangled
high up in the mansion's Bing cherry tree with
its luscious fruit. Remembers
the lavish blooming. Remembers the caves they
built in the cellar, in the masses of clothing and draperies.
Tunnels to each other's kingdom with their stolen
jewelry and scarves. It was always summer, except for
the night when his father suddenly appeared. Bursting
in with crates of oranges or eggs, laughing in a way
that thrilled them. The snowy night behind him.
Who never brought two pounds of anything. The boy remembers
the drunkenness but not how he felt about it,
except for the Christmas when his father tried to embrace
the tree when he came home. Thousands of lights,
endless tinsel and ornaments. He does
not remember any of it except the crash as his father
went down. The end of something.

Samuel Green

GRANDMOTHER, CLEANING RABBITS

I shot this one by the upper pond of the farm
after watching the rings trout made rising
to flies, watching small birds pace the backs
of cows, hoping all the time she would run.

My grandmother told me they damaged her garden.

I think it was a way to make the killing
lighter. She never let me clean them, only asked
I bring them headless to her. I bring this one
to the fir block near the house, use the single-
bitted axe with the nick in the lower crescent
of the blade, smell the slow fire
in the smoke-house, salmon changing
to something sweet & dark. A fly turns
in a bead of blood on my boot. I tuck
the head in a hole beside the dusty globes
of ripened currants, talk quiet to the barn cat.

In her kitchen my grandmother whets the thin blade
of her Barlow, makes a series of quick, clever cuts, then tugs
off the skin like a child's sweater. This one was
pregnant. She pulls out a row of unborn rabbits
like the sleeve of a shirt with a series of knots.
The offal is dropped in a bucket. Each joint gives way
beneath her knife as though it wants
to come undone, as though she knows some secret
about how things fit together. I have killed
a hundred rabbits since I was eight.

Samuel Green's most recent collection is *The Grace of Necessity* (Carnegie Mellon University Press). He was recently named as the first Poet Laureate of Washington State. This is his second appearance in *Alaska Quarterly Review*.

This will be the last.

I am twenty, & about to go back
to the war that killed my cousin in Kin Hoa,
which is one more name she can't pronounce.
I haven't told her about the dead,
and she won't ask. She rolls the meat
in flour & pepper & salt, & lays it
in a skillet of oil that spits like a cat.
She cannot save a single boy who carries a gun.
All she can do is feed this one.

Rachel Hadas

THE PILOT LIGHT

The angers flare up suddenly, blue flames.
Sometimes I can predict what sets one off,
and the dismal precision of this knowledge
angers me afresh:

the innocent struck match
and what it chances this time to ignite;
and underlying every exchange,
meek, deceptive, low, the pilot light.

Rachel Hadas is the author of many books of poetry, essays, and translations. Her latest book of poems is *The River of Forgetfulness* (2006), and her new prose selections can be found in *Classics* (2007).

John Haines

EPITAPH FOR A YOUNG MAN

I seemed always standing
before a door
to which I had no key,
although I knew it held behind it
a gift for me.

Until one day I closed
my eyes a moment, stretched,
then looked once more.
And not surprised, I did not mind it
when the hinges creaked
and, smiling, Death
held out his hand to me.

John Haines is the author of ten collections of poetry including *At the End of This Summer: Poems 1948–1954* (Copper Canyon Press, 1997); *The Owl in the Mask of the Dreamer* (1993); and *New Poems 1980–88* (1990), for which he received both the Lenore Marshall Poetry Prize and the Western States Book Award. He has also published a book of essays entitled *Fables and Distances: New and Selected Essays* (1996), and a memoir, *The Stars, the Snow, the Fire: Twenty-five Years in the Northern Wilderness* (1989). "Epitaph for a Young Man" was chosen last year by Ted Kooser for his "American Life in Poetry" weekly column. This is his third appearance in *Alaska Quarterly Review*.

Tony Hoagland

ENDEARMENT

Going down the stairs
I call her *sweetiepiecup*,
and remember who else I used to call that,
into whose cup I poured my sweetieness

And how then I took my watering can
to another garden
and continued my life,
or rather, my life continued me,
– my life, as Basho said, "on which I floated like a leaf,"

though less gracefully than that –
thrashing a little,
accidentally inhaling some dirty riverwater,
banging sideways into the pilings of the bridge,
but going on nonetheless,

saying things
no tough guy would ever say
and then saying them again.

We use the same words
because it's the same sentiment
that flows through us now as then
and you could keep your mouth shut

for the sake of your aesthetic standards,
and then you would be

Tony Hoagland won the 2005 Mark Twain Award from the Poetry Foundation, for humor in American poetry. His books of poems include *What Narcissism Means to Me*, *Donkey Gospel* and *Real Sofitikashun*.

a highly principled
beacon of stupidity.

As for me, it's too late to pretend
to be a genius at affection;
I'm just a pedestrian of love

who found out en route
what destination means.

It all boils down to
words like marzipan and muffinhead,
Miss Potato Pancake and butterlips,

these terms of endearment
we scatter about us
wherever we go

which weigh almost nothing
like ashes, or little flowers.

THE TRUTH

In summer there was some malfunction in the wasps
that wanted to get inside the screened-in porch.
It sent them buzzing against the wire mesh,

probing under the eaves
crawling into the cracks between the boards.
Each day we'd find new bodies on the sill:

little failures, like struck matches:
shrunken in death, the yellow
color of cider or old varnish.

The blue self of the sky looked down
on the self of the wooden house
where the wasps were perishing.
The self of the wind swept them to the ground.

The wasps seemed to be extensions
of one big thing
making the same effort again and again.

I can remember that feeling of being driven
by some need I could not understand
to look for a passage through,

– trying again and again
to get inside. I must have left a lot
of dead former selves scattered around behind

me while I kept pushing my blunt head
at a space that prevented my entering
– and by that preventing, delivered me here,

to where I live now,
still flying around in my head,
dissatisfied

in the land of the unfinished.

THE LONELIEST JOB IN THE WORLD

As soon as you begin to ask the question, *Who loves me?*,
you are completely screwed, because
the next question is *How Much?*,

and then it is hundreds of hours later,
and you are still hunched over
your flow charts and abacus,

trying to decide if you have gotten enough.
This is the loneliest job in the world:
to be an accountant of the heart.

It is late at night. You are by yourself,
and all around you, you can hear
the sounds of people moving

in and out of love,
pushing the turnstiles, putting
their coins in the slots.

Paying the price which is asked,
which constantly changes.
No one knows why.

CAPTIVITY NARRATIVE

When I was 17, 20, 24, and 29 1/2,
I said to myself, again and again,
while gazing upwards at the blue, empty-headed sky,
or sometimes while staring hard
at the back of my own unwrinkled hand,
"Life is a dream."

Now I repeat to myself nearly every day,
with a fierce, almost brutal
desire to persuade my listener,
"This is *real*,"

and this would be,
as you've heard of "captivity narratives,"
a "maturity narrative,"
except for the fact that
I mean now exactly the same thing
as I did back then.

Ilya Kaminsky

MS. VERONINA

As our neighbor Veronina walked across
her balcony one of the soldiers

said oh and stood and
another stood and the whole battalion

Veronina's son collected
silver coins with the president's profile

and she watched
hours pass from bombs in the public garden to bombs

on the theater balcony. Then what, to olive trees?
Hours pass

she understood it better than I did
hours pass

from olive tree to olive tree.
And Veronina touched

her son's hair & said it better than I can
our kind prostitute from

apartment 8b, *you are not*
going to cry about it not in front of them.

Ilya Kaminsky is the author of *Dancing in Odessa*, which won the Whiting Writers'
Award, American Academy of Arts and Letters' Metcalf Prize, and Ruth Lilly Fellow-
ship from *Poetry* magazine. It was named Best Poetry Book of 2004 by *ForeWord Magazine*. This is his second appearance in *Alaska Quarterly Review*.

We let them take her, all of us cowards,
what we did not say

we carried in our suitcases, our coat-pockets, our nostrils.
They took you, Veronina.

And I see myself –
a man's hand writes on the white brick wall

of an apartment building "People
live Here" like an illiterate

signing a document
he does not understand.

Ted Kooser

OH, MARIACHI ME

All my life I have wanted nothing so much
as the love of women. For them I have fashioned
the myth of myself, the singing troubadour
with the flashing eyes. Always for them
my black sombrero with its swinging tassels,
this vest embroidered with hearts, these trousers
with silver studs down the seams. Oh, I am
Mariachi me, as I had intended. I am success
and the price of success, now old and dusty
at the edge of the dance floor, still smiling,
heavy with hope, clutching my dead guitar.

Ted Kooser is the author of ten collections of poetry, including *Delights & Shadows* (Copper Canyon, 2004); *Winter Morning Walks: One Hundred Postcards to Jim Harrison* (2000), which won the 2001 Nebraska Book Award for poetry; *Weather Central* (1994); *One World at a Time* (1985); and *Sure Signs* (Pittsburgh, 1980). His fiction and nonfiction books include *Braided Creek: A Conversation in Poetry* (Copper Canyon, 2003) written with Jim Harrison; and *Local Wonders: Seasons in the Bohemian Alps* (2002), which won the Nebraska Book Award for Nonfiction in 2003. Kooser's poem, "Oh, Mariachi Me," one of twenty-one annual valentines published since 1986, will be a part of his forthcoming book, *Valentines,* from University of Nebraska Press. Kooser is a former U.S. Poet Laureate and Pulitzer Prize winner.

Maxine Kumin

THE WINKING VULVA

When the old broodmare came down with Cushings, an end-
of-life disease, they took in a friend's

retired gelding, thinking to have a companion
for their own midlife gelding when

the time came to put her down. The mare sprang
into action, newly young,

squatting, crooking and lifting her tail,
squirting urine and winking her vulva, all

classic signs of estrus. Although
bewildered, the newcomer seemed to enjoy

her slavish attention. What old boy
wouldn't? But when in the sweltering

heat her heat persisted, they worried: something
endocrine amiss, an ovarian tumor?

Consulted, the vet only laughed, *good for her!*
At last the inviting vulva gave

Maxine Kumin's sixteenth poetry collection, *Still to Mow,* was published in 2007. She is
also the author of a memoir, *Inside the Halo and Beyond: The Anatomy of a Recovery* (W. W.
Norton, 2000); four novels; a collection of short stories; more than twenty children's
books; and four books of essays. Kumin is a former U.S. Poet Laureate and Chancellor
of the Academy of American Poets. She has been awarded the Harvard Arts and Robert
Frost medals, and a Pulitzer Prize in poetry. Kumin is a contributing editor of *Alaska
Quarterly Review.*

up its vigorous winking, the two big guys
lowered their heads side by side to graze.

Between them, regally in charge, the mare
until *rough winds do shake* and bid no more.

Lance Larsen

MAKE OF ME

Dirt combed free of snarls twice a day,
tree trunks white washed as high
as arthritis can reach.

Make of me, late fall, what this peasant
has made of her poverty.
Flung potato water gleaming on bricks

outside her window,
an albino dog licking up wet
holiness, legs splayed to keep its paws dry.

Lance Larsen's third collection of poems is forthcoming from the University of Tampa
in 2008. His recent work has appeared in *Georgia Review, Orion, Prairie Schooner*, and
Salmagundi.

Dorianne Laux

WESTERN LIT

The goats of Greece ate heart-shaped leaves
from the vineyards of the gods, offending them.
From that day forward their slaughterers wrote goat songs,
epic plays, great tragedies in which many humans died.
Blindings, stabbings, betrayals, mistaken identity.
The goats were ecstatic! They leapt in the fields.

Dorianne Laux's fourth book of poems, *Facts About the Moon* (W. W. Norton), is the recipient of the Oregon Book Award. Her first book, *Awake,* was recently reprinted by Eastern Washington University Press. Red Dragonfly Press will release *Superman: The Chapbook* in 2008. She is a contributing editor of *Alaska Quarterly Review.*

LEARNING TO DRIVE

The long miles down the back road
I learned to drive on. The boy riding
shotgun. His hand on my hand on

the gear shift knob. Our eyes locked
on the dusty windshield, the cracked
asphalt, old airstrip, the nothing spreading

for miles: scrub brush, heat waves, sky
a few thin contrails. His patience
endless. My clumsiness: the grinding

gears, the fumbled clutch. The wrench of it
popped like an arm from its socket.
His blue, beloved '67 Ford lurching

into the dirt. I was 16. He was older.
His football-player shoulders muscular,
wide. Where did he get his kindness?

Why spend it on a girl like me:
skinny, serious, her nails bitten, her legs
bruised. Hours under summer's

relentless heat. His car stumbling
across the barren lot until I got it,
understood how to lift my left foot,

my right hand, in tandem, like dancing,
which I never learned to do, never wanted
to turn circles on the polished floor

of a dark auditorium, the bleachers
hemming me in. I drove toward the horizon.
Gravel jitterbugging under his tires. Lizards

skittering. Jays lifting to the buzz
of telephone wires. He taught me
how to handle a car, how to downshift

into second, peel out from a dead stop.
His hand hung from the open window,
fingers clamped on a lit cigarette,

trailing smoke. We couldn't guess
where we were going. He didn't know
he was flying to Vietnam

and I was on my way out of there,
The Byrds singing *Eight Miles High*
when he turned off the radio

and told me to brake, opened his door
and slid out to stand on the desert road,
to let me go it alone. His back pressed

against all that emptiness.

Phillis Levin

THE OTHER RHINOCEROS

Actually, there were two
It is spelled the same in the singular
Or the plural

Now there is one

What is the plural of flood
Does more water make it plural
No, only more water in more places

A flood
A big flood
A great flood

Water
The water
The waters rising

And no ark
No dove
No branch of an olive

Live
Olive tree
Live

Phillis Levin is the author of three books of poetry, *Temples and Fields*, *The Afterimage*, and *Mercury*, and is the editor of *The Penguin Book of the Sonnet*. Her fourth collection, *May Day*, will be published by Penguin later this year.

O live
Olive
O live

Note: "The Other Rhinoceros" is one of two poems sparked by an article in *The New York Times* on August 14, 2002, reporting on a flood that broke the banks of the Vltava river, the biggest natural disaster in modern Czech history. The front-page story included a photograph of a blindfolded rhinoceros being lifted out of the water. The second rhinoceros, the article explained, "turned violent and had to be killed."

NOT A PRAYER

in memoriam CZESŁAW MIŁOSZ

On Lorenzo Lotto's suffering Christ
There are two tears, two drops of blood,
But now that I've heard of your passing

They glimmer differently. Was this
Your gift? For I cannot tell if
The flickering shadow of what is gone

Makes this happen, bare fact suffusing
The skin until our pulse quickens
With the life of another running in

Our own vessels, sending out
Its fluctuating rhythm, a flock of birds
In a net of chance, a shape – of what?

Now that you're on the other side, lifting
An eyebrow at the view, you would know
What to say. Your bridge that is made

Out of prayer, those feet walking over
The river into a cushion of crimson
Anemones . . . Will you find her there,

That girl on the metro, smiling
An aisle away? Does a waiter turn,
Flashing a silver tray? If only I could fall

Into the arms of my father, asking him
Why he is sad, so that he may weep
The tears he never shed as we marvel

At the symmetry of two drops of water,
Two drops of blood – Lotto's brush
A chrysalis of dust, a butterfly

Who gave herself back to original light
So the worm again can fly. Every mote
Is a spasm of sight, every wound an eye.

Anne Marie Macari

PARADISE CAME OVER ME ONCE

Paradise came over me once. A grove
of tall eucalyptus trees, long red leaves

we picked off the ground, animals following us.
His voice echoing among the trees, naming

everything, filling the silence with brittle
kingdoms: moon-faced owls, finches, a dead mouse,

core of an apple. He couldn't stop himself.
I mocked him: earlobe, nipple, throat. He floated

from me, brooding like the huge trees with their
gigantic solitude. I turned away.

For a long time we had been enough: what I'd
later name happiness. Sweet kernel within

my despair. Don't ask why. Think of your own hunger,
how it gets worse no matter what you feed it.

Anne Marie Macari's most recent book is *Gloryland*, published by Alice James Books in 2005. Her book, *Ivory Cradle*, won the 2000 *American Poetry Review* / Honickman first book prize. Her poems have been published in *TriQuarterly, American Poetry Review, Five Points, The Iowa Review,* and *Field*.

Morton Marcus

BEFORE & AFTER

After our breathing stilled
and the slippery patina
cooled on our skins, I imagined
us lying side by side
like two separate statues
imbedded in marble,
as if we were half formed,
never to emerge from rock.
It hadn't been that way
the moment before
when we were one, bucking
against each other, fighting
our separateness until it
finally gave up for a moment
and let us fall through
each other's entangled arms.
"What are you thinking?" I asked.
"Nothing" you replied.
What is it I wanted words to say
where words had no place,
where knowing was not knowing?
Like the vase by the open window
that fell in a sudden gust.
Remember? Two green parakeets
were painted on it
amid scrolling red vines.
We didn't hear it
until it shattered, that vase
we could not replace.

Morton Marcus is the author of ten books of poems. *Pursuing the Dream Bone* appeared in 2007. His literary memoirs, *Striking Through The Masks*, will be published in the spring of 2008. His work has been included in over 88 anthologies in the United States, Europe and Australia.

Stefanie Marlis

SOUTHWESTERN SUITE

I could tell it was warmer this morning, even before I opened the door. Without the heat on, the house wasn't ice, and now, an hour after turning it on, birds are singing in the yard.

* * *

All my life it seems I've tried to feel others' pain, and now and then I accomplish this. The dog looks up at me, a burr – what we call a goat's head – lodged in her paw, and I can't take one more step. When I saw Peter for the last time, speech slurred, his body shaky and exposed, the man he was roomed with – a huge Buffalonian twice his size – complained behind the hospital curtain. I didn't feel Peter's pain, I felt him feeling all of mine, and the huge Buffalonian's.

* * *

While I lived in a small mountain town in Arizona, my father died, my only family. I came to love horses in that place. A special five grazed the pastures of an in-town ranch, and it was easy to see that they needed one another. Sometimes all five would stand close, in a horsy pinwheel, their tails swatting flies.

* * *

Sick for weeks, in early light, I saw Gautama Buddha silhouetted under the Bodhi tree, hair knotted upon his head. For a second I thought: "A sign!" The bun was a warped cactus pad, the body a stunted prickly pear trying to get a foothold beneath a tall, greening chamiso on the edge of a gray arroyo.

Stefanie Marlis is the author of a recent collection of poems, *Cloudlife*, published by Apogee Press. This is her second appearance in *Alaska Quarterly Review*.

* * *

A tiny southwestern restaurant serves Spanish and American food next to the car wash. I have guacamole, chips, and a side of beans. Two waitresses and the owner all attend to me. The place is immaculate: squares of color advertising Corona beer hang like prayer flags above the counter.

* * *

A man wearing no hat crosses a sun-struck field in New Mexico: "Come on the happiness of my life. Come on the happiness of my life," he repeats, and a small dog trots up to him.

Linda McCarriston

ANNIVERSARY

I thought last night – all of it
from day-deepened-as-
champagne-does-into-cognac

to sleep – that it was my heart only
leaning into my chest, shoulder
of my heart pressing, trying the door to

what? Place blood comes from?
Heat? Cold? Weight? Gravity
that *down* won't satisfy but

over will, *out, against, around*?
But it was not I think now
only mine but yours too; it was

across what death erects,
dark matter. You are – as before
you only incompletely were–

breast to breast with me, trans-
fusing pulse: systole. Diastole
mine. I felt the half of it.

Linda McCarriston is the author of three collections of poems, *Talking Soft Dutch*, an Associated Writing Programs Award Series selection, *Eva-Mary*, winner of the Terrence Des Pres Prize at Northwestern University, and *Little River*. Her poems have appeared in *The Atlantic, Poetry, Poetry Northwest, The Ohio Review*, and *New England Review*.

Christopher Merrill

L'ANCIEN RÉGIME

for Sarah Rothenberg

Of the condemned. Of nectar, and a necklace
Of olive shells strung through a chandelier,
And the nomenclature of the last regime
Replaced with ruthless inefficiency
By the henchmen of the new idealists.

Of an order filled for a photographer
Who dropped his pocket watch from the draw bridge
Into the lookout of a wooden yacht
Returning from an auction in Antigua –
An order for Kalashnikovs and Stingers.

Of the intervals between light and dark, defined
As challenges to the prevailing styles
Of thought, worship, decorum. Of desperate measures
That saved no one. Of fossils catalogued
And sold to a collector. Of the condemned.

Tell it again, without embellishment:
How they watched a kettle of turkey vultures
Scavenging in the wetlands, woods, and scree
Below the dam slated for demolition,
And did not mourn their decision to dissolve
What they had held in trust – the farm; the arts
Of storytelling, husbandry, and love;
The household gods instructing them to work
Without recourse to bitterness or blame
For well-made things undone by chance, by weather.

Christopher Merrill's books include *Brilliant Water* (poetry) and *Things of the Hidden God: Journey to the Holy Mountain* (nonfiction).

A vulture on a boulder flapped its wings
And lifted off into the blackening
Sky of an early winter. *They smell something,*
He said. She shrugged. *They must smell something, no?*

To separate the heavy gas molecules from the light, one
isotope from another, hundreds of aluminum cylinders and
rotors, magnets and gears, were shipped to a warehouse in
Kuala Lumpur, where a team of engineers built centrifuges
for clients in Pyongyang and Tehran and Tripoli. The way of
the world, said the deckhand loading the unmarked crates
onto a freighter registered in Panama, which had caught the
eye of a pirate fishing in the Straits of Malacca. Where they
might end up was anybody's guess.

Say the equation's wrong: $x = y$
Unless there is no hope for a reply

From your beloved, God, the universe.
Neither at nightfall, nor on the abyss

Will you discover what was integral
To what you left behind: your soul. That model

Was never part of the experiment:
That we could build a tower of cement

From which to plot an assault on the oasis
Settled and squandered by our enemies.

And so we set fire to the covered bridge,
Which dropped into the water like a language

Destined to be forgotten. Conjugate
The lessons that we never learned: how late

And wrong we were, how slow to realize
That there were other forms and other ways

Of being in the world: $x = y$
Until a plume of ash undoes the sky.

W. S. Merwin

THE SILENCE OF THE MINE CANARIES

The bats have not flowered
for years now in the crevice
of the tower wall when the long twilight
of spring has seeped across it
as the west light brought back
the colors of parting
the furred buds have not hung there
waking among their dark petals
before sailing out blind along their own echoes
whose high infallible cadenzas only
they could hear completely and could ride
to take over at that hour
from the swallows gliding
ever since daybreak over the garden
from their nests under the eaves
skimming above the house and the hillside pastures
their voices glittering in their exalted tongue
who knows how long now since they have been seen
and the robins have gone from the barn
where the cows spent the summer days
though they stayed long after the cows were gone

W. S. Merwin has published over twenty books of poetry. His recent collections include *Present Company* (Copper Canyon, 2007); *Migration: New & Selected Poems* (2005) which won the 2005 National Book Award; *The Pupil* (2002); *The River Sound* (1999), which was named a *New York Times* Notable Book of the Year; *Flower and Hand: Poems 1977–1983* (1997); *The Vixen* (1996); and *Travels* (1993), which received the Lenore Marshall Poetry Prize. In 1967, Merwin published *The Lice*, followed by *The Carrier of Ladders* in 1970 which received the Pulitzer Prize. He has also published nearly twenty books of translation, including *Sir Gawain and the Green Knight* (2004), *Dante's Purgatorio* (2000), and volumes by Federico García Lorca and Pablo Neruda. His numerous plays and books of prose include *The Lost Upland* (1992); *Summer Doorways* (2006); and *The Book of Fables* (2007), a collection of his short prose. He is a former Chancellor of the Academy of American Poets and has served as Poetry Consultant to the Library of Congress.

the flocks of five kinds of tits have not come again
the blue tits that nested each year
in the wall where their young
could be heard deep in the stones by the window
calling Here Here have not returned
the marks of their feet are still there on the stone
of their doorsill that does not know
what it is missing
the cuckoo has not been heard
again this May
nor for many a year the nightjar
nor the mistle thrush song thrush whitethroat
the blackcap that instructed Mendelssohn
I have seen them
I have stood and listened
I was young
they were singing of youth
not knowing that they were singing for us

FAR ALONG IN THE STORY

The boy walked on with a flock of cranes
following him calling as they came
from the horizon behind him
sometimes he thought he could recognize
a voice in all that calling but he
could not hear what they were calling
and when he looked back he could not tell
one of them from another in their
rising and falling but he went on
trying to remember something in
their calls until he stumbled and came
to himself with the day before him
wide open and the stones of the path
lying still and each tree in its own leaves
the cranes were gone from the sky and at
that moment he remembered who he was
only he had forgotten his name

Joseph Millar

FIRE

When Axel starts humping the Coupe de Ville's trunk
in Michael Cimino's *The Deer Hunter*
America raises its iron voice
over the coal fields of Pennsylvania:
backyard engine blocks, chain hoists,
bell housings, toothed gears
resting in pans of oil – stammering out
the poem of combustion,
bright tongues and wings, white-hot ingots
glimpsed in the huge mills by the river,
coke ovens, strip mines, brick stacks burning
over the spine of the Appalachians.

Carnegie, gifter of libraries,
Frick with his Rembrandts, his Titians,
both fast asleep in the arms
of the strikebreakers
under the ashes and slag.
Fire with no roots, no memory,
grooved steel running all night to Detroit,
fire of the profit line, fire of the shareholders,
I-beams, pistons, fenders and chrome.

Joseph Millar's second collection of poems is *Fortune,* from Eastern Washington University Press. Recent poems appear in *Shenandoah, DoubleTake, TriQuarterly, Ploughshares,* and *Manoa.* This is his fourth appearance in *Alaska Quarterly Review.*

Paul Muldoon

QUAIL

Forty years in the wilderness
of Antrim and Fermanagh
where the rime would deliquesce
like tamarisk-borne manna

and the small-shot of hail
was de-somethinged. Defrosted.
This is to say nothing of the flocks of quail
now completely exhausted

from having so long entertained an
inordinately soft spot for the hard man
like Redmond O'Hanlon or Roaring Hanna

who delivers himself up only under duress
after forty years in the wilderness
of Antrim and Fermanagh.

Paul Muldoon is the author of eleven collections of poetry including *New Weather* (1973), *Mules* (1977), *Why Brownlee Left* (1980), *Quoof* (1983), *Meeting The British* (1987), *Madoc: A Mystery* (1990), *The Annals of Chile* (1994), *Hay* (1998), *Poems 1968–1998* (2001) and *Moy Sand and Gravel* (2002), for which he won the 2003 Pulitzer Prize. His eleventh collection, *Horse Latitudes*, appeared in the fall of 2006. A Fellow of the Royal Society of Literature and the American Academy of Arts and Sciences, Muldoon was given an American Academy of Arts and Letters award in literature for 1996.

Leonard Nathan

AN OLD MAN

An old man that sleep has deserted, strokes
the cat curled in his lap and writes a sonnet –
A what! Next, you'll say he holds a candle
to the sun, or re-invents the music box.
Does he imagine that the ancient form
will yield him up as-yet unpublished truth
if he can just stay faithful to its rites:
eight lines out toward death, six to get back
again to life – a beautiful imbalance
to the end? – Hopeless, I think, he circles
round again through the same old theme: love
too late except to understand. Well,
let him be, and let the cat sleep on,
its all-consuming dream, to it, no dream.

Leonard Nathan (1924–2007) was the author of fourteen books of poetry. A posthumous volume, *Ragged Sonnets,* will be published by Orchises Press at the end of 2008.

Dennis O'Driscoll

BIRDING

How dainty the wren's working parts
must be, how miniature the brain-chip
which triggers its alarm, how tiny
the furnace that keeps its heart warm.

* * *

A perfect touchdown
on the hazel tree:
not as much as a
raindrop is dislodged.

* * *

Living at a hectic pace,
    swallows feed on the move
        grazing the long acre
            of the air.

* * *

A one-for-sorrow magpie,
rough diamond, on the grass.
And two greenfinches:
consolation enough.

* * *

Numbers in decline, dawn choruses
learn to manage with more modest forces
like authentic performances of Bach.

Dennis O'Driscoll's eight books of poetry include *Reality Check* (Copper Canyon Press, 2008). He has edited a collection of contemporary quotations about poetry: *Quote Poet Unquote* (Copper Canyon Press, 2008). His awards include a Lannan Literary Award in 1999, the E. M. Forster Award from the American Academy of Arts and Letters in 2005 and the O'Shaughnessy Award for Poetry from the Center for Irish Studies (Minnesota) in 2006.

* * *

The blue tit's mate
keeps watch,
flexing wings,
while eggs – little
bigger than heart
pills – incubate.

* * *

An inspired touch: the red beak
on the black swan – like the yellow
bill toning down the blackbird's
austere image (the same blackbird
I catch raiding my strawberries:
a burglar red-handed at the till).

* * *

Or for vulnerability
a swan afloat in sleep
resting on the feather
mattress of itself.

* * *

Pigeons, beer-bellied
bruisers, hang out
on the pavements
of building ledges
or stare up and down:
small-town shopkeepers
on a slack weekday.

* * *

Jackdaws curse from a height,
flying off with scoffing sounds
when their protection racket is disturbed.

* * *

A cock pheasant strides
into your life, sweeping
away despair with a flick

of its aristocratic tail,
the illuminated manuscript
of its chest a prophetic text.

* * *

How time flies on May evenings
when you hear birds
belt out sentimental songs
for sheer entertainment.

Sharon Olds

SIBLING UNRIVALRY

What does it say that my sister was so
relieved to see me, as if she'd been waiting, all her
seventeen months, for me to be born.
It helped that our mother did not love me
to excess – maybe every second child
of the same sex as the first is post-modern.
And it helped that I was humorous,
and savored my sister's solemness,
and her black Prince Valiant helmet of hair.
And I liked the way my shoulders fit
inside her encircling arm, me in a
small sweater, miniature of the
one she wore, which next year I would wear.
And to walk with her was like walking beside
an Egypt barge, she glided, and I could be the
little fireworks set off from the barge.
Dressed for church, the Junior Mints of our
four Mary Janes asparkle,
I'd cavort beside her. I loved it that she seemed
not baffled, she seemed to know. Now, I can
see it, her dear melancholy,
no one knowing to ask her, How are you
really. But what I saw, then,
was her steadiness – like a young, slightly sorrowing
mother, to me – how could I not
thrive, bad in the shadow of her goodness?

Sharon Olds is the author of eight poetry books including *The Dead & the Living* which
received the National Book Critics Circle Award. She is completing a new collection
called *O Western Wind*. Her poetry has appeared in *The New Yorker, The Paris Review*,
and *Ploughshares*, and has been included in more than one hundred anthologies. Olds
held the position of New York State Poet from 1998 to 2000. She is currently a Chancellor of the Academy of American Poets.

Without her, I might be in a river,
or a sea, or be lightless ashes in air.
When we meet, now, we gaze and savor.
She remembers me as fragile, and as
the one who came to her, in her iso-
lation, and saved her.

Alicia Ostriker

WINTER TREES

February I am like the trees
not ruined exactly but shorn of ornament
and destitute of motivation

it is possible to find
both beauty and truth in their
pure forms

and I would like to do so
in myself if time could be persuaded
to hold off its heartless green

Alicia Ostriker is a poet and critic, author of eleven volumes of poetry. Her most recent book of poems is *No Heaven* and her most recent prose work is *Dancing at the Devil's Party: Essays on Poetry, Politics, and the Erotic*. This is her second appearance in *Alaska Quarterly Review*.

Michael Palmer

HIDDENNESS

(Kansai plains)

To enter the temple we had to pick the locks,
put off our shoes, sing to sleep the clocks
watching us.
Peel your skin back
from the top
and pass through the chamber of clouds,
of peonies, elms and pale herons,
of emperors long dead
therein assembled,
the silent, the wild-eyed,
the meek and the violent,
the awkward and the graceful dead
therein assembled.
Entering the temple the rain will follow
and come to rest
there, above your head.
It will lave memory,
it is said,
then ask its one question.
About the hours,
their parts?
A space of time, might we say,
that a glimpse
will not contain?
Count the silent stones
if you can
and the ringing drops.

Michael Palmer's most recent book of poetry is *Company of Moths* (New Directions, 2005). In the spring of 2007, a chapbook, *The Counter-Sky* (with translations by Koichiro Yamauchi), was published by Meltemia Press of Japan, to coincide with the Tokyo Poetry and Dance Festival. His selected essays, *Active Boundaries*, will appear later this year from New Directions.

Linda Pastan

A DOZEN ROSES

Their stems in the glass vase
are the color
of beet greens,

and their tight purplish blooms
the size and shape
of summer beets.

If only you had brought me
beets instead of
these formal flowers.

If only you had dressed them
in oil and lemon,
caressed them

with sour cream,
we could feast until
our mouths were as red

as the beets themselves,
then bruise those mouths
saltily against each other.

Linda Pastan is the author of *Queen of a Rainy Country* (W. W. Norton, 2006); *The Last Uncle* (2002); *Carnival Evening: New and Selected Poems 1968–1998* (1998); *An Early After-life* (1995); *Heroes In Disguise* (1991); *The Imperfect Paradise* (1988); *PM/AM: New and Selected Poems* (1982); *The Five Stages of Grief* (1978); and *A Perfect Circle of Sun* (1971). From 1991 to 1995, she served as the Poet Laureate of Maryland. This is her second appearance in *Alaska Quarterly Review*.

LILACS

I have followed the lilacs
cluster by
purple cluster

from Whitman's
dooryards in April
north to New York

where my mother's garden
drowns in their scent
even without her.

I remember her gathering them
by the armful, blossoms
as plump and pale

as lavender pillows,
the white ones
paler still, shedding

their tiny florets
like baby teeth
over her polished floors.

Now in late May
somewhere near Boston
they are still blooming,

their leaves as heart-shaped
as memory itself.
If I keep traveling north,

I may finally find myself
somewhere beyond the treeline,
beyond loss.

For though I don't believe
in ghosts, I am haunted
by lilacs.

RACHMANINOFF'S ELEGY

for William Lyoo

Though only 16,
you played the piano

at your mother's funeral,
to honor her, you said,

and the music was like water
washing over a wound,

each note a footfall
through a darkness

you will negotiate
for years.

Robert Pinsky

SHAME

(Purgatorio XXX, 61–78)

I turned at the sound of my own name, to see
That same veiled lady as at the festival
Of angels. She too turned, and looked at me

From across the water. The folds of cloth that fell
From her encircling crown of Minerva's leaves
Concealed her face, but I heard her voice: *Look well—*

In the regal, even tone of one who saves
Her most heated words for later, she began—
Be sure: I am Beatrice. Can you say what gives

You courage, or happiness? Or made you plan
To climb the mountain? What has brought you here?
I dropped my gaze to the water, but looking down

I saw my own reflection, clear in that clear
Mirror—and I flinched and looked away again.

Robert Pinsky is the author of several collections of poetry, most recently *Gulf Music: Poems* (Farrar, Straus & Giroux, 2007); *Jersey Rain* (2000); *The Figured Wheel: New and Collected Poems 1966–1996* (1996), which received the 1997 Lenore Marshall Poetry Prize; *The Want Bone* (1990); *History of My Heart* (1984); *An Explanation of America* (1980); and *Sadness and Happiness* (1975). He is also the author of several prose titles and two acclaimed works of translation: *The Inferno of Dante* (1994), and *The Separate Notebooks* by Czeslaw Milosz (with Renata Gorczynski and Robert Hass). From 1997 to 2000, he served as the U.S. Poet Laureate and Consultant in Poetry to the Library of Congress. He is currently a Chancellor of the Academy of American Poets.

Donald Platt

LOOKING FOR MY FATHER IN AIX-EN-PROVENCE, EARLY MARCH

I.

I look for my father in the open-air flea market along the Cours
  Mirabeau, where they sell raw silk scarves of all colors and
  straw baskets of all shapes and sizes

* * *

I finger the silk, let it slide across the back of my hand to feel its
  nubbly smoothness

* * *

I imagine carrying home a dozen brown eggs, russet potatoes, and
  leeks in a new shopping basket with one cane dyed red, woven
  in and out among the white undyed canes like a ribbon running
  around its circumference

* * *

I look and look but buy nothing

* * *

I do not find him at the fountain where the naked stone boys ride
  dolphins that jet water from their mouths

* * *

They turn the fountains off after midnight

Donald Platt's third book, *My Father Says Grace,* was published in spring 2007 by the
University of Arkansas Press. His poems have recently appeared or are forthcoming in
Another Chicago Magazine, Antioch Review, AGNI, Michigan Quarterly Review, and
BOMB. This is his fourth appearance in *Alaska Quarterly Review.*

* * *

I look for him at the all-night boulangerie where I buy a crusted
   baguette "de la festivale" with pointed ends and afterwards
   walk the dark narrow cobbled streets, eating as I go

* * *

I do not find him, my ghostly boulevardier in his white-on-white
   pinstriped suit, strolling with the crowd along the Avenue
   Victor Hugo, which changes its name to the Boulevarde du Roi
   René, then to the Boulevarde Carnot, to the Cours Saint Louis,
   to the Boulevarde Aristide Briand, to the Cours Sextus, to the
   Avenue Napoléon Bonaparte before becoming the Avenue
   Victor Hugo again

* * *

He does not linger over and savor the truite almandine at the table
   next to the door at the Brasserie Carillon

* * *

He does not flake its flesh from the small bones with his fork

* * *

He is fog clinging like lamb's wool to the steep terraced hillsides
   early in the morning

* * *

No, he is the smoke from the brush fires that farmers tend with
   metal rakes as they burn off their land

* * *

No

* * *

He is neither of these

* * *

He is not among the cypresses that stand like dark torches on either
   side of the gate next to the snarling sandstone lions

* * *

I look for him among the rows of pollarded plane trees that line the
    streets and throw their late-afternoon shadows on the cream-,
    gray-, or orange-tinged limestone walls of 15th-century houses

* * *

Their shadows are those of upraised hands with fingers
    outstretched, beseeching blessing

* * *

I look for my father's sermons among the spray-painted black and
    pastel hieroglyphs of graffiti on the ancient stone walls

* * *

I find only "Antoinette, On T'Aime"

* * *

Antoinette, whom everybody loves

* * *

I look for him at the salon de thé, where a pregnant woman
    drinks black tea from Sri Lanka, which tastes like smoke from
    burning eucalyptus branches, and dips almond macaroons into
    her cup

* * *

While she drinks, she gives suck to her first, year-old child who
    guzzles and slurps the thin sweet milk from her white, blue-
    veined, globed left breast

* * *

Her husband with the three-day beard is slim, beautiful, and
    attentive

* * *

He bends across the table toward her

* * *

What do they say to each other

* * *

They are so young

* * *

How will they live their lives

* * *

I look for my father on the "Impasse Fleurie," which translates as "enflowered cul-de-sac"

* * *

Only the pear trees are blossoming, levitating in the backyards of houses with red tile roofs

* * *

They float there like cast-off bridal veils

* * *

The one stout palm tree's fronds rustle in the wind

* * *

I could say that the mistral roughs up my hair like a father running thick clumsy fingers through his son's hair, but I would be wrong

* * *

The mistral through the cypresses makes the sound of surf on a white beach three thousand miles away

II.

I look for my father behind the red double doors of Cézanne's studio on the hill at Les Lauves

* * *

The red paint is flaking

* * *

The brass handles have been polished to the dull luster of lake water at dawn by one hundred and five years of hands opening and shutting those doors

* * *

Inside I find only three skulls on a gray chest of drawers

* * *

Three green bottles, one of turpentine, one of linseed oil, and one
   half full of red wine, the vin ordinaire

* * *

The rotting fruit Cézanne loved to paint in his still lives – shriveled
   apples, pears, lemons

* * *

A bowl of small yellow onions, which have sloughed off their dry
   papery skins

* * *

I've always loved how "still life" translates into French as "nature morte"

* * *

My father is the one streak of royal blue among the smeared greens,
   yellows, reds, ochers, and grays on Cézanne's rectangular palette

* * *

The thin pine palette has warped, gone wavy

* * *

Its one thumb hole is a Cyclops' blind eye off-center

* * *

All that's left of Cézanne in this room is one pencil drawing of a
   skull and four half-finished watercolors – one of a vase of irises,
   another of a row of eight large flower pots with shrubs growing
   from them, another of a white plaster Cupid without arms, and
   one of a river with thirteen naked male bathers

* * *

Next to the watercolor Cupid stands the plaster cast

* * *

Neither is more real than the other

* * *

All that's left of Cézanne is a black cap with a visor, his black bowler, his
   everyday olive overcoat, his black wool Sunday coat, and two
   umbrellas hanging on pegs by the door, waiting for him to go out

* * *

He will not return

* * *

It is not raining today

* * *

All that's left of Cézanne is his olive work smock flecked with blue, white, and gray paint

* * *

The only thing that lasts is sunlight flooding through the thirty large panes of glass that form the studio's northern wall

* * *

The long shadows we cast near dusk, our short shadows at noon

Alberto Ríos

THE BOY WHO BECAME A MAN WITH POCKETS

1.

Putting something in his pockets began simply enough.
A young man, first it was a black comb.

A new brown wallet followed, his own house key,
Some spare change, a small knife –

The gift of an 18th birthday, the last way left
His parents could say, *take care of yourself.*

These were not any longer the quartz and igneous rocks,
The green-backed, still-moving beetles,

The chewing gum prizes saved of childhood.
These were new pockets, bigger pants and new ideas.

The things in his pockets grew up as he grew up.
The key soon enough imagined its need for a key chain,

And not simply something plain. Perhaps a companion key,
As well, the back shed's key, that grizzle-toothed brass finger.

The small knife, everyone agreed, would be elegant in a sheath,
A nice, three color plastic-lace braid hanging from it.

Alberto Ríos is the author of six volumes of poetry including *The Theater of Night* (Copper Canyon Press, 2005); *The Smallest Muscle in the Human Body* (2002); *Teodora Luna's Two Kisses* (1990); *The Lime Orchard Woman* (1988); *Five Indiscretions* (1985); and *Whispering to Fool the Wind* (1982), which won the 1981 Walt Whitman Award. Other books by Ríos include *Capirotada: A Nogales Memoir* (University of New Mexico Press, 1999), *The Curtain of Trees: Stories* (1999), *Pig Cookies and Other Stories* (1995), and *The Iguana Killer: Twelve Stories of the Heart* (1984), which won the Western States Book Award. This is his second appearance in *Alaska Quarterly Review*.

2.

The wallet set up an entire business of its own, quickly
Under its own management and with no board of directors:

It gathered cards for all manner of transaction and recognition,
Allowance and identification, direction and appointment.

It gathered photographs and coupons, paper money at last,
And everything else that might be prodded into folding.

The pockets looked like the cheeks of a chipmunk,
And were big enough to give him the aspect of a pontoon boat.

On most days he began to walk more slowly,
But on windy days nobody could keep up with him.

He started to look for pants with more pockets,
Or rather, he had to look for them.

A handkerchief, which he never used, some balled-up tissues
He thought he would use, but didn't use either,

Sometimes a small book, or his lunch, a sandwich,
Some cookies, and some potato chips.

3.

His new pockets filled just as quickly as the old ones.
He could never wear shorts.

And finally he could not sit.
He tried, but it was easier not to.

And then it was easier not to walk so much at all.
Instead, people came to him.

They came at first to offer consolation, to assure him
It was not unusual, this richness of circumstance, really.

But consolation was soon followed by reward,
Unexpected – a knife sharpening, a new pair of socks,

All the things he had and which they needed.
And they were curious things, not things

Readily available anywhere else, not in stores,
Certainly. These were the things found in drawers,

Discarded at first, or saved for later,
Then suddenly and altogether necessary.

4.

He could not walk but he gave flight to so many others,
A lightness of spirit at having found something

Irretrievably lost otherwise. He gave happiness
Where others had thought to give it to him.

This was the bargain, then, that he made with the world.
He would keep the small things at his side

In exchange for the big things not seeing him,
Not needing him, not paying him any attentions.

And it was a kind of life, free of tigers and danger,
But love, too, free of that and not entirely satisfying.

A bargain was a bargain, however, and his life was calm.
It was a full-enough life, a way to move, a way of breathing

Without moving. He became something else,
Not himself. A place, a garden, a store,

Everything but what he had been – a little boy
Believing in the necessary things of the world.

Pattiann Rogers

A BLIND ASTRONOMER IN THE AGE OF STARS

He considers himself lucky to have been born
during the Age of Stars, all those beings
in their shimmering shades still flaring, their silent,
untouchable presence. He imagines how
they shine as if they were the work of light
giving sight, like eyes, to a blind universe.

Making his way through fields at night,
he can feel the light from those million
sources touching him like the particles
composing the finest airy fog, touching him
like the knowledge of lives in a silent forest.
He feels each star in the way he hears
each syllable of his lover's whisper.

And he claims to see the constellations
from the inside out, having been inscribed
from birth, he says, with their configurations.
Indeed his Braille depictions of Canis Major,
Dorado, Lyra, Orion, are to scale and perfect.
Often through summer nights, he lies on open
hillsides to observe the heavens. He describes
the stars as transforming his body with their patterns
like tattoos of light – the wings of Cygnus,
the horns of Taurus. What kind of fortune
would it be, he wonders, to feel the light
of the Southern Cross along his brow?

Pattiann Rogers is the author of thirteen books of poems. Her latest, *Wayfare,* will be
published later this year. It will include "A Blind Astronomer in the Age of Stars."
Rogers received a Literary Award from the Lannan Foundation in 2005 and is a contributing editor of *Alaska Quarterly Review.*

He believes that the constant *jeetz-a-jeetz*
of the wayside crickets and the notes of the reed
toads sounding like whistles underwater
and the soft-bristle brush of grasses in the wind,
all together match in cadence the multiple
spacings and motions of the stars. He imagines
that the sudden piercing cry of a rabbit or a prairie
mouse at night corresponds to the streak of a falling
meteor, a helpless descending diagonal of light.
He hears their passing in this way. The earth,
he is certain, is related to the starry sky by blood.

By the solid black existing behind his eyes,
he understands the dimension beyond the edge
of the farthest horizon, that place whose light
has not had time to reach and touch him. He knows
that place, its state and its lack. One he calls
Patience, the other *Pity*.

Kay Ryan

BOMB FISHING

One bomb
and the fishing's
done. Up come
the fish, displayed
upon the sea
as upon a tray:
yellow; grape;
some metal
like the sun;
green-striped;
stippled rose;
blue-grey.

Kay Ryan has published several collections of poetry, including *The Niagara River* (Grove Press, 2005); *Say Uncle* (2000); *Elephant Rocks* (1996); *Flamingo Watching* (1994); *Strangely Marked Metal* (1985); and *Dragon Acts to Dragon Ends* (1983). Ryan's poems have appeared in *The New Yorker, The Atlantic, Poetry,* and *The Paris Review*. Her work has been selected four times for *The Best American Poetry* and was included in *The Best of the Best American Poetry 1988–1997*. She is currently a Chancellor of the Academy of American Poets. This is her second appearance in *Alaska Quarterly Review*.

Umberto Saba

THE GOAT

I talked to a goat.
She was alone in a pasture, and tethered.
Stuffed with grass, soaked
by the rain, she bleated.

That monotonous bleating was brother
to my sorrow. And I answered, first
in jest, then because sorrow is eternal,
has one voice and never changes.
I heard this voice in the wails
of a solitary goat.

In a goat with a semitic face,
I heard all other pain lamenting,
all other lives.

(translation by George Hochfield and Leonard Nathan)

Umberto Saba (1883–1957), the pseudonym of Italian poet and novelist Umberto Poli, is now regarded as one of the most important Italian poets of the first half of the 20th century. About the translators: Leonard Nathan (1924–2007) was the author of fourteen books of poetry and numerous translations from a variety of languages. George Hochfield has translated three works of Italian prose published by Northwestern University Press. A large selection of Saba's selected poems, translated by Nathan and Hochfield and accompanied with biographical and critical materials, will be published in 2008 by Yale University Press.

Peter Dale Scott

MARIANNA

(Poem to my first grandchild)

Buddha face you will quickly lose
for a face like the rest of us
a mask of self

what is it you remember
that composes you
to look so serenely inward?

With my own children I thought
weighed down by self-importance
of what I could give them

now as my mind empties
I see it is you
who give to us

We stare in amazement
as your newborn breaths displace us
nudging us towards that silence

where the long line of children
who in their turn became parents
prepare a space for us

Peter Dale Scott's poetry includes the three volumes of his trilogy *Seculum: Coming to Jakarta* (1988), *Listening to the Candle* (1992), and *Minding the Darkness* (2000). In 2002 he received the Lannan Poetry Award.

All we ever spoke for
has come back to infancy
the predestined past

Peggy Shumaker

BUGLER, FT. WAINWRIGHT, ALASKA

Yellow leaves in July. Damn.
A single osprey banks over birches, cruises
upriver and down. Birch bark splits like the lip
of the bugler hitting a high note
the morning after Tiffany
with a tongue like a mouthful of tadpoles
and a hardhat she neglected
to mention. Gashed knuckles.
He pictures a nicotine chip, his tooth
stuck in an itchy keloid baptized with blood.
No fieldworker with a short-handled hoe
ever had a back that hurt this bad, each vertebra
burnished by fire, each bone a glowing coal, ruby
spine searing inside him. His breath sinks
in and in and in, shriek held back.
Forced through brass his pain
ices over echoed notes of "Taps."

Peggy Shumaker is the author of six collections of poems: *Blaze,* a collaboration with
painter Kesler Woodward (Red Hen Press); *Underground Rivers* (Red Hen Press); *Wings
Moist from the Other World; The Circle of Totems; Braided River;* and *Esperanza's Hair.* Her
memoir, *Just Breathe Normally,* was published by University of Nebraska Press in 2007.
Shumaker is a contributing editor of *Alaska Quarterly Review.*

CHECKLIST

He pushes up so a sample of av gas
gushes into the cylinder,
checks to make sure
no water's dripped in.

Our lives depend on this,
two engines propelling us
over the Tanana Flats,
above the bump bump

Joe creates bouncing
above the dotted Arctic Circle.
We have information Bravo
warning us

but we already know
a single sandhill crane
could knock us
out of the sky – not even

a winged one that big –
a bufflehead, a camprobber even,
or a sheer drop of air
or a burst hydraulic line

iced wings, a crystal
in the fuel line,
nicked prop, a flat tire,
burst vessel

in plane or pilot,
quick spiral
we take on faith
won't happen

today, and that's how
we get clearance
for take off, lean
into pure power

let earth spin below
without us on it.

Gerald Stern

SAVE THE LAST DANCE FOR ME

When it comes to girls the Chihuahua
on Ninth Street going down to
Washington on the left side
below the Hong Kong Fruit,
he knows where he's going, between their
beautiful legs, his eyes
bulge a little, his heart,
because he is small, surges,
explodes too much, he is
erotic, his red tongue
is larger than a squirrel's, but
not too much, nor does he
walk on a wire with fresh
ricotta in his mouth nor
an apple they sell for a quarter,
a bit of rot on one side but
sweet underneath the skin, more
Macintosh than not, he
loves Velveeta, he knows
the price of bananas, he whines
when there is a death; there was one
drowning in a sewer,
his owner gave me five dollars
for lifting the lid with a hammer
and going down into the muck
when I was twelve, it was
my first act of mercy

Gerald Stern is the author of fourteen books of poetry including, *This Time: New and Selected Poems,* which won the National Book Award in 1998 and his latest book of poems, *Save the Last Dance for Me,* in late spring of 2008. He was the first Poet Laureate of New Jersey, serving from 2000 to 2002 and received both the 2005 Wallace Stevens Award for mastery in the art of poetry, and the 2005 National Jewish Book Award for poetry. He is currently a Chancellor of the Academy of American Poets.

and she gave me a towel
that matched the Chihuahua's towel
and ah he trembled containing
such knowledge and such affection
and licked my face and forced me
to shut my eyes, it was
so much love, his whole
body was shaking and I,
I learned from him and I
learned something once from a bird
but I don't know his name
though everyone I tell it to
asks me what his name was
and it is shameful, what
was he, a dog? The Klan
was flourishing all the while
we dreamed of hydroelectric
so we were caught in between
one pole and another and
we were Hegelian or just
Manichean, we kept
the hammer on top of the manhole
so we could lift it to get
our soft balls and tennis balls
though he who weighed a pound
could easily fall into
the opening, such was our life
and such were our lives the last
few years before the war when
there were four flavors of ice cream
and four flavors only; I'll call him
Fatty; I'll call him Peter;
Jésus, I'll call him, but only
in Spanish, with the "h" sound,
as it is in Mexico;
Jésus, kiss me again,
Jésus, you saved *me*,
Jésus, I can't forget you;
and what was her name who gave me
the towel? and who was I?
and what is love doing in
a sewer, and how is disgrace
blurred now, or buried?

Chase Twichell

SAVIN ROCK

What I know is a slur of memory,
fantasy, research, pure invention,
crime dramas, news, and witnesses
like the girl who liked to get high
and the one who was eventually
returned to her family unharmed.
The rest I made up.

The fathers drank beer in the grandstand,
flattening cans and dropping
the dull coins into the underworld.
It was daylight – we went right under,
down into the slatted dark,
the smell under the bleachers
where lots of men peed,
paper cones and dead balloons,
people jostling and whispering.
Down there were the entrances
to the dark rides, the funhouses:
Death Valley and Laff-in-the-Dark.
Of course that's not true;
they were right on the main boardwalk
under strings of bulbs lit up all night.

Mom says, *To remember something,*
go back to the place where you forgot it.
But the place was torn down
forty years ago; there are motels
there now, where the Ferris wheel

Chase Twichell is the author of six books of poetry, the most recent of which is *Dog Language* (Copper Canyon, 2005). *A New & Selected* collection is forthcoming, also from Copper Canyon.

lurched up and over the trees,
over the fathers at their picnic table
close enough to feel the Tilt-a-Whirl's
crude rhythms through the ground.
They make the cars go faster or slower, depending.
After hours the boys loosen up the machines
and take girls for rides.

Hey kid! I flipped a coin in my head
and it came up tails. Want to take a walk?
He looked older than our parents.
How old did our parents look?
He was fifty, or thirty. I remember
the smell of whatever he put on his hair,
and the blue nail on his thumb.
He could flip a lit cigarette around
with his lips so the fire was inside.
I rode a little metal car
into Laff-in-the-Dark to dance
with the skeleton (possibly real
since some teeth had fillings)
that flung itself at me from the dark.

A dog watched me from a pickup window.
The World's Biggest Pig lay
beached on its side, heaving.
The tattooed lady had a tattooed baby.
No one ever tattooed a newborn child
for real, did they? The "Chinese Dragon"
was only an iguana.
The go-cart man asked me if I wanted
a little on the side. I said no.
His friend in the bleachers
blew me a kiss.
In the Maze of Mirrors
I was fatso and skeleton,
skirt blown up by a fan. Not true.
A fan blew a girl's skirt up.
It wasn't me. I was a tomboy. I wore pants.

At the stable girls in love with horses
visited and groomed and fed them daily.
For girls it was about trust,

being part of a couple,
the horse and the girl,
but for the man in the barn
it was about making girls feel
groomed and visited.
Come on over here. Didn't a guy ever
brush your hair with a currycomb?
I don't believe it! Not once?
Little honeycomb like you?
And kittens, always good bait.
A little dish of spoiled milk.
Do you think they don't pass them around?
They pass them around.
Marked kids get shared,
little pink kid tongues *lick lick licking*
like a puppy! Good dog!
And on the carousel a man appeared
from nowhere to help her on,
hand palm up on the saddle just as she sat,
squirming there until the horse pulled her away.
Little cowgirl, giddyup!

Thus she became half human half animal,
and remained so her entire life,
now a shepherdess, now a sleek young
she-goat, so lithe and small-hipped,
half tame, little goatskin haunches –
hand-fed on SnoCones and cotton candy –
the girl who was eventually
returned to her family unharmed.

Tell me, little shepherdess,
how this bodes for first love,
the centaur pissing outside your tent
in the afterlife, having come down
over the stony pastures to claim you
and feed you trout and fiddleheads
and take you to bed on the high ledges
where the wind holds you down for him.
But he won't be the first.

Sweet-sharp bouquet of darkroom,
holster with toy six-gun,

hot umbrella lamps nudged into place
by his fat pink fingers.
A little maraschino light presides over
negatives strung up like game to dry.
The tomboy's showing her rump,
hard little buttocks under the tender wrapping,
the skin. Little wonton.

Jean Valentine

TRAVELLER

A matchbox painted & figured
with five gardeners
and thirty-seven flowers, red & blue,
a pretty garden.
One little fellow stands off.
Anybody can see
love is all around him,
like the blue air. Most
dear in the Double Realm
of paint, he is a traveller.
He stands off, alone.
When somebody dies, as is the custom,
he burns the place down.

Jean Valentine is author of eight books of poems, most recently *Little Boat* (Wesleyan). Her collection, *Door in the Mountain: New and Collected Poems 1965–2003*, was awarded the 2004 National Book Award for Poetry.

Rosanna Warren

FIRE

for Avigdor Arikha

Smoldering coal and Burgundian scarlet, the velvet couch
on which models have sprawled for more
than thirty years under the laser beam
of your gaze, the predatory flick of your brush:

that was the fire that mattered. That was the touch
that set your pulses stuttering, hair
springing in sweat beads, pupils flecked in flame
at the woman's body poured out as white ash.

Such longing never fits its frame. Her top hip's pitched
to one side, an arm's flung wide – the rug
collides with the canvas edge. You are consumed,
consuming. In the new self-portrait you glare

from your barbecued brow, your alizarin scorched
temple and irradiated jowl, your mug
outraged, your wide iris subsumed
in an ice glint at the core of turquoise fire.

Rosanna Warren's most recent book of poems is *Departure* (Norton, 2003). Her book of criticism, *Fables of the Self: Studies in Lyric Poetry,* will be published by Norton this fall.

Robert Wrigley

BISON

The slenderest of winds walks
among them as they graze, can even be seen

urging them along, herding them almost,
among the vastnesses. Placid, massive,

theirs is the locomotion of planets
or stars, slow boulders in the river's quick.

All day they have come and gone, a million or more
similarly humped and haunched, their bellies
a darkening blue, swollen with rain.

Robert Wrigley is the author of *Earthly Meditations: New and Selected Poems* (Penguin, 2006); *Lives of the Animals* (2003); *Reign of Snakes* (1999), winner of the Kingsley Tufts Award; *In the Bank of Beautiful Sins* (1995), winner of the San Francisco Poetry Center Book Award; *What My Father Believed* (1991); *Moon in a Mason Jar* (1986); and *The Sinking of Clay City* (1979). This is his third appearance in *Alaska Quarterly Review*.

FLOWER

It was a party trick for company at first,
though he came to love the sawed-off tablespoon
bit just beyond his upper lip and filled
with ruby-colored hummingbird food.
The fractious, belligerent broadtails
feinted at his monolithic face then hovered
and sipped so close he could feel
their petal wings buffeting his cheeks.
And when in the spoon's shined concavity
only a tear's worth of red remained,
always one truculent hummer would sit rimside
and suck the last of it up, then rise
to study his eye, blinked open like a day-
blooming deep brown flower
from which it intended also to sip.

Al Young

IN PRAISE OF SPIRIT

You're a natural, baby. A chorus and choir
all unto yourself, you require no coaching.
You reach and yank out hidden meanings long
before big questions arise; no stretch, no yes,
no no; you simply know the score before the game
gets played or called. You hold back nothing.
If I so much as think about phoning you at two, three
or four o'clock in the church-like countdown to dawn,
you beat me to the punch. You inch your way
into my listening presence, our heart-speak well
within earshot. You never read me the riot act,
you cite neither chapter nor verse. Instead
you read me the way our ancestors read the river
or the pasts and futures of leaves. Consider this:
your kiss; the lazy, spaced-out solar systems encircling
its sun. Distilled deep inside your labial caresses
the root-wet light of joyousness listens to me
and to all the rest of what we still call the world.
To sermons of the marketplace, you don't say amen;
you don't say *shhh* and you don't shout. Baby,
you do exactly what you know. You move. You shine.

Al Young is the author of four collections of poetry including *Heaven: Collected Poems,*
1956–90 (1992), *The Blues Don't Change: New and Selected Poems* (1982), *Geography of the*
Near Past (1976), *Some Recent Fiction* (1974), *The Song Turning Back into Itself* (1971), and
Dancing: Poems (1969), which won the Joseph Henry Jackson Award. He has also published five novels and four memoirs including *Bodies and Soul: Musical Memoirs* (1981),
which won the American Book Award. This is his second appearance in *Alaska Quar-*
terly Review.

C. Dale Young

LA REVANCHA DEL TANGO

In my mouth, song. In my ear, your own song:
so much *amor*, this dance . . . The chin cocked

to facilitate a side-long glance, the arch
of the back, the quick spark of Santa Maria

that races from thigh to knee to ball of the foot,
the stamp, that singular sound, the sound

of *you-will-have-me-tonight*. Arch
of the back, the return of your body

to mine. Spanish guitar, the slicked-back
black hair, and Santa Maria of the evening

who invites all that is forbidden in public:
the hand on shoulder, the hand on back,

on waist, the perspiration a glue
between curve of hand and the curve

of the neck. Santa Maria of Argentina, I pray
to you, to this beautiful man who follows

my lead. No flowers, no rose in my teeth.
I carry only song in my mouth.

C. Dale Young's collections of poetry are *The Second Person* (Four Way Books, 2007) and *The Day Underneath the Day* (Northwestern, 2001).

What some call lust, others call *the calculation*.
We were fooled by the Virgin, by the music's

instructions to love. Santa Maria of Argentina,
flower behind her ear, the mouth about to sing

the song of laughter. Virgin-goddess, necessary whore –
There is, indeed, a subtle logic to seduction.